From the maelstrom of a sundered world, the Eight Realms were born. The formless and the divine exploded into life. Strange, new worlds appeared in the firmament, each one gilded with spirits, gods and men. Noblest of the gods was Sigmar. For years beyond reckoning he illuminated the realms, wreathed in light and majesty as he carved out his reign. His strength was the power of thunder. His wisdom was infinite. Mortal and immortal alike kneeled before his lofty throne. Great empires rose and, for a while, treachery was banished. Sigmar claimed the land and sky as his own and ruled over a glorious age of myth.

But cruelty is tenacious. As had been foreseen, the great alliance of gods and men tore itself apart. Myth and legend crumbled into Chaos. Darkness flooded the realms. Torture, slavery and fear replaced the glory that came before. Sigmar turned his back on the mortal kingdoms, disgusted by their fate. He fixed his gaze instead on the remains of the world he had lost long ago, brooding over its charred core, searching endlessly for a sign of hope. And then, in the dark heat of his rage, he caught a glimpse of something magnificent. He pictured a weapon born of the heavens. A beacon powerful enough to pierce the endless night. An army hewn from everything he had lost. Sigmar set his artisans to work and for long ages they toiled, striving to harness the power of the stars. As Sigmar's great work neared completion, he turned back to the realms and saw that the dominion of Chaos was almost complete. The hour for vengeance had come. Finally, with lightning blazing across his brow, he stepped forth to unleash his creation.

The Age of Sigmar had begun.

CONTENTS

DESIGNED BY GAMES WORKSHOP IN NOTTINGHAM

British Cataloguing-in-Publication Data. A catalogue record for this book is available from the British Library. Pictures used for illustrative purposes only.

Games Workshop Ltd., Willow Road, Lenton, Nottingham, NG7 2WS, United Kingdom

Printed by 1010, in China.

games-workshop.com

THE STORMCASTS

A new age has dawned, heralded by the arrival of a new army. They are heroes reforged into legend, the embodiment of a living tempest cast from Azyr, the Celestial Realm. They are Sigmar's wrath made manifest – the Stormcast Eternals. They have entered the Mortal Realms for but a single purpose: war!

The heavens roar and the sky itself is rent by searing bolts from above. With a flash of lightning and rolling thunderclap the gleaming warhosts of the Stormcast Eternals arrive for battle.

Their weapons wreathed in crackling arcs of lightning, the Stormcasts launch their assault. It is as swift as it is brutal. Heavy hammers rise and fall, a shield-shattering onslaught that batters down all who stand before it.

The Stormcast Eternals fight as warriors born, like legends from ancient song. Each and every one of them is a hero clad in armour of nigh-impenetrable sigmarite, yet they fight not as individuals but as a unified force, each retinue moving and striking as one. Advancing in lockstep, the shield wall of the Liberators presents an impenetrable barrier. Over that mobile bastion blazes a hail of stormbolts, as Judicators shoot death from afar. The Retributors target the most formidable foes, each strike from their great mauls releasing the storm's energies in a blow that could fell an Aleguzzler Gargant. Above, streaking upon wings of light, Prosecutors hurl hammer-headed bolts before diving down to join the fray.

All Stormcasts enter battle with calculating precision, yet there is no mistaking their emotions. Behind their stern, expressionless masks, underneath their resplendent armour, dwells a thunderous tempest. For the Stormcast Eternals fight not just for Order, or for mankind, or even for almighty Sigmar himself. They fight for vengeance. All long to avenge the depredations that Chaos has inflicted upon their peoples and their lands. Theirs is a fury that is barely contained.

The Stormcast Eternals are made for battle. Once they were mortal men, but they were taken to the Heavens and reforged by Sigmar, imbued with a portion of the glory of the gods themselves. Hard he crafts them, tempering each with justice and the raw energies of the storm. Upon the Anvil of the Apotheosis they are gifted with superhuman strength and courage beyond the ken of mortal man.

Only after long toil did Sigmar cast forth his new army. It was a bolt of purest order to sear through the darkness, a storm of righteousness to battle the all-conquering night. Never before had such an army been seen. Here was a force to stand against the bloodthirsty and debased horrors of Chaos. With hammer-strike fury the Stormcast Eternals entered the fray. So was the Age of Sigmar begun.

At first, Vrak had been pleased to face a true adversary. Few tribesmen dared challenge the Bloodhorns, and those that did proved unworthy. He laughed to remember those frail-limbed foes whose weak blades shattered upon his gore-encrusted armour – he had carved through them like so much meat and they had broken, begging him for mercy. Yet these new foes – the gleaming ones that strode forth from out of lightning itself – they were not afraid. They stood as tall as his own hulking warriors, and it was difficult to look directly upon them, for even beneath the darkened skies their armour gleamed. Again and again Vrak brought down his great two-handed axe, delivering blows that should have shivered his foe's shield and hacked him in twain. Yet, impossibly, the shield held, the strikes rebounding harmlessly in showers of sparks. The enemy, his helm a golden mask, spoke not a word, responding neither to Vrak's challenges nor his curses. 'What are you?' Vrak shouted, his berserk fury draining out of him as something crept into the red frenzy of his mind. It was a new sensation, and it was very much like doubt.

The first to feel the wrath of Sigmar's new armies were the Chaos invaders in the Igneous Delta.

Striding from out of the lightning strikes, the gleaming Stormhosts brought war, swift and terrible. Long had the Chaos conquerors held sway, the oppressors glutting themselves upon the lifeblood of the just. Now, with each glowing hammer strike, the Stormcast Eternals fought to cast down the darksome forces, to reclaim the lands in the name of Sigmar. Never in their long years of domination had the minions of Chaos been so challenged, never had they fought armies such as those that now assailed them.

The storm started in Aqshy, but quickly spread to all other realms. From high up in his sky palace in the Heavens, Sigmar cast forth more lightnings. Again and again incandescent bolts seared down, hurling more Stormcast Eternals into battle.

At long last, Sigmar's Storm had broken. Once begun, there could be no turning back.

SIGMAR ALMIGHTY

The Lord of the Storms, Sigmar Heldenhammer is by far the most powerful of mankind's deities; he is the Great Uniter, the God-King who presided over the Great Alliance. It is he who rules the Celestial Realm of Azyr, and he who created the Stormcast Eternals.

At the end of the final battle for the world-that-was, Sigmar fell into darkness. Only by clutching onto the last remnant of his world did he escape destruction. Only by his unyielding will did he hold onto that metal core.

Long was Sigmar's journey through the sea of stars. At last he was saved by Dracothion the Great, Father of Star Drakes. Many are the tales that recount how Dracothion befriended Sigmar, helping him hang the metal core in the sky above the Realm of Azyr. It was Dracothion that showed Sigmar the Eight Realms, and so began what is now known as the Age of Myth.

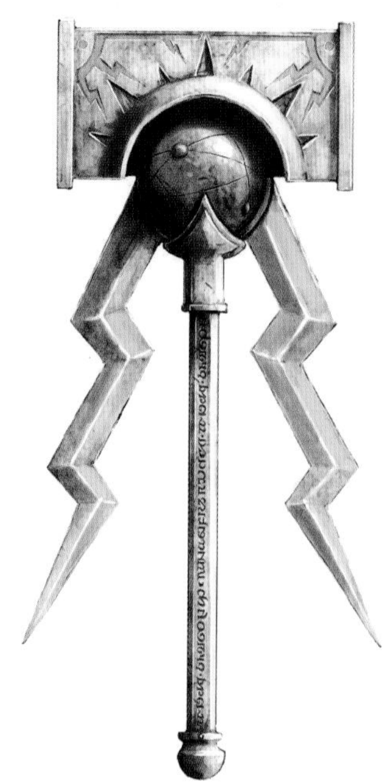

Many legends are told of Sigmar's deeds during this period, such as when he felled Ymnog, King of Gargants, hunted down Great Nagendra, the shape-shifting realm serpent, and when he bested the greenskin god Gorkamorka in feats of strength. Indeed, Sigmar found and awakened many other gods, creating a pantheon over which he ruled. Cites were founded and civilisations flourished. Yet Chaos came, bringing war and plague, corruption and ruin. After long wars and many defeats, Sigmar's pantheon broke, and he retreated to seclusion in the Realm of Azyr, sealing the gates behind him.

Few speak of the tale of how Sigmar came to lose Ghal Maraz, his rune-enchanted warhammer, because few survived the Battle of Burning Skies.

The first Chaos incursions cut deep into the Eight Realms. Cities fell before the daemonic onslaught, yet always Sigmar, or one of his pantheon, led a counter-attack to drive off the invaders. Each of the greater daemons that led the Dark Gods' armies was defeated in its turn. Sigmar cast down the Khornate armies of An'ggrath, matching their rage against his might. He smote Feculox, most immense of Great Unclean Ones, within of the City of Branches. Through the power of his immortal soul, the God-King fought off the magicks of the Lord of Change, Kiathanus. Luxcious the Keeper, first to call herself Ur-Slaanesh, withered in the face of his unbreakable resolve.

Later, it was Archaon, the Everchosen, who united the four powers, bringing the greater daemon champions together upon the Fireplains of Aqshy. Their combined armies covered the horizon, reaching into the sky itself – for they tore a rent in reality, from which poured daemons beyond count. The gods assembled before that fell host, and the battle that followed shook the realms.

From above the advancing legions Nagash summoned necromantic armies, while Gorkamorka rampaged unstoppably. The burning light of Teclis banished foes unnumbered, yet it was mighty Sigmar, always at the pantheon's fore, that turned the tide. None could stay the God-King, and Ghal Maraz smote each of the enemy commanders in turn, until Sigmar faced Archaon. The God-King hurled his hammer at his fell foe, but he was deceived. Tzeentchian illusion bent his aim, so that Ghal Maraz entered the rift, never returning. Without his matchless hammer, Sigmar and his forces were doomed to defeat. The disasters of the Nexus Wars ensued, following which Sigmar retreated, shutting the Gates of Azyr behind him. For long years he dwelt upon his losses, simmering with rage and plotting how he might one day reclaim his own.

THE DOMINION OF CHAOS

Chaos spread across seven of the Eight Realms. Only the Realm of Azyr was safe from the all-conquering armies, yet the Dark Gods remained unsated. Boundless was their hunger for destruction. All lands and peoples must be corrupted, mercilessly ground beneath their iron tread.

The early Chaos invasions had been horrific, but after Sigmar shut himself within the Realm of Azyr, they became far worse. A black and terrible darkness fell over the realms, for truly the Age of Chaos had arrived.

By attacking and controlling the Realmgates – mystic portals that allowed travel between the different realms – the Chaos forces cut off and dominated all who opposed them. One by one, the greatest civilisations were pulled down into ruin. Some fell to sword and fire, others to plague or decadent corruption from within. Warped creatures crept from the shadows to live amongst the rubble-strewn vestiges of what had once been high and mighty. These foul things whispered to the huddled and desperate survivors – telling them that their gods had abandoned them. There was, however, still a way to regain that former glory.

Some of the broken bands of people resisted, and the majority of these were hunted down, so they might be slain or enslaved. Others began to worship the Chaos Gods, swearing dark vows and joining grotesque rituals. Across the realms abhorrent monuments rose, towering to the skies, and fell fortresses were constructed atop the old ruins. The Chaos forces grew so powerful the lands themselves began to warp, changing under their corrupting influence. The Dark Gods, sure of victory yet always grasping for more, began to fight amongst themselves, each striving to be the sole conqueror.

The gods waxed and waned in power and ascendancy as their plots ripened. Khorne, the Blood God, Nurgle, God of Plagues and Tzeentch, Master of Sorcery – each controlled lands untold. Slaanesh, the God of Excess, was missing, although his minions were ruthless in searching for their absent deity. Even the Great Horned Rat, God of the Skaven, claimed vast kingdoms. It was Khorne, however, who emerged as the most powerful of all. Everywhere his armies ran rampant, mercilessly slaughtering all they found.

AZYRHEIM, LAST OF THE FREE CITIES

Each of the realms once boasted many great cities, civilised places full of wonder. Since the Age of Chaos, they have been ransacked many times over, save only Azyrheim, which stands eternal. It is the last great bastion of Order, a walled city, renowned not just for its size and splendour, but also for its citizens. There, communities of mankind, aelf, duardin and many others dwell. Many came as refugees, fleeing their own embattled realms before Sigmar commanded the Gates of Azyr to be shut. Others trace their line of descent from times more ancient still, bitter remnants of the world-that-was displaced out of home and time. Although Azyrheim's citizens come from different nations, they are united by a common hatred of Chaos, and by dreams of one day reclaiming their lost lands. Many armies of retribution have vowed to march out from Azyrheim, joining the Stormcast Eternals as they seek revenge against the minions of the Dark Gods.

SIGMAR

For many centuries the mightiest of mankind's warriors have been whisked off battlefields, called to a higher cause. In thunder flashes, those chosen are taken to Sigmaron amongst the stars of the Celestial Realm. Great and perilous trials await.

In the Age of Myth, Sigmar awoke many gods, each of which gave unto him a gift, and Sigmar pulls energies from those divine tributes to impart to each warrior he reforges. After a lengthy feast to build up their strength, the aspirants are taken to the Chamber of the Broken World to be blasted apart by lightnings, then reformed. Those that survive begin the godly infusion, the mettle of each man sorely tested time and again within the Forge Eternal.

Seven times seven are the Cairns of Tempering which the aspirants have to weather. Steeped in justice, and blended once more with godly gifts, those battered spirits that awaken still have an ultimate test. Upon the Anvil of the Apotheosis are Stormcast Eternals finally wrought. If they endure they rise a final time, imbued with the energies of the heavens, bequeathed a gleaming portion of the God-King Sigmar's own divine powers.

FORGED FOR BATTLE

Sigmar forged his new army for war – to battle the minions of the Dark Gods and to reclaim the oppressed realms. The Stormcasts were the light of reason to counter the malign forces that ruled as conquering over-tyrants. The blessings of celestial lightning imparted more than just great strength of mind and body to each Stormcast. In each of them is instilled a surety of purpose stronger than that of even the most magnificent of mortal heroes. They are Sigmar's Heralds of Righteousness, those who will mete justice to the corrupted realms.

To equip his Stormcasts, Sigmar demanded arms worthy of the gods themselves. The God-King called upon the Six Smiths, and they clad the new warriors in armour of sigmarite – interlocking plates wrought of enchanted metal hewn from Mallus itself. Weapons too they fashioned, capturing the living tempests of Azyr and binding them within warhammer and blade. Every blow struck with weapons of such matchless artifice unleashed thunderclap power; every skybolt arrow echoed the lightning's fury. So were entire Stormhosts armed for battle, resplendent in their gleaming panoply of war.

In the Gladitorium the Stormcast Eternals trained, forming a warrior brethren that fought as one. Diverse formations meshed, blending more than just tactics and armaments, for they learned to harness the celestial energy Sigmar had imparted to them, and lent their thunder-charged might to each other's arms. The Stormhosts scoured Azyr of the wicked creatures and ferocious monsters which lingered there still, becoming a military machine the likes of which had never been seen before. Only then did Sigmar declare the Stormhosts ready to face the true foe. Only then did Sigmar unleash his storm of vengeance and send forth his Stormcast Eternals to battle.

It was the duardin Forge-God Grungni who caught and shaped the raw magics of the Celestial Realm for Sigmar. By ascending to Sigendil, high above the sky palaces, the God-King could hurl those bolts down into the Mortal Realms. From out of those meteoric strikes strode forth his vengeance – the gleaming and indomitable armies of the Stormcast Eternals.

Thus by lightning did the Stormhosts bring war, swift and terrible, to the Chaos invaders. Yet such rapid deployment was both a gift and curse. Once delivered unto realms far distant, the Stormcasts could not return to the Heavens in the same manner. After their initial lightning assaults, only by victory or death could Sigmar's warriors come once again to the realm of Azyr.

If the Stormcast Eternals seized a Realmgate, then they could use it to travel back to Azyr in triumph, leaving some of their number to secure their gains. Failure in their mission meant only death, in which case their immortal souls would blaze in rapturous flashes, their spirits returning to the Heavens to be reforged once more by their mighty maker.

BATTLES OF THE FIRST STORM

The Stormcast Eternals were born of Sigmar's vision of an army capable not just of standing before the despoiling armies of Chaos, but of defeating them. When at last Sigmar loosed his thunderbolts, the wrath of the Stormcast Eternals was felt across every realm. Thus was born a new age of battle...

THE CLEANSING

After the Gates of Azyr were closed campaigns were fought to rid the realm of evil. Enclaves of orruks and creatures which bore the taint of Chaos were hunted down, first by the armies of Azyrheim and then by the newly formed Stormhosts. Mythic beasts remain in Azyr to this day, but none bear any trace of corruption.

UNSHACKLED

Many tribesman had refused to bow before the domination of Chaos. The majority had been slain, yet not all. At the vast slavepits of Ashlyon, millions toiled ceaselessly, worked unto death. Led by the Hammers of Sigmar and the Knights Indomitable, the Stormhosts brought celestial fire and vengeance down upon the slavers.

THE GLADITORIUM

Not all training was monster hunting. A gift from Malerion, the enchanted dome of the Gladitorium enabled the Stormcasts to fight each other, yet arise unharmed when battle was done. In the greatest exercises entire Stormhosts were pitted against each other in thunderous war drills.

THE FIRST BLOW

Sigmar opened his war in the Brimstone Peninsula, where Vandus Hammerhand's Thunderstrike Brotherhood seized the first of the Gates of Azyr. Soon strikes were landing in dozens of locations.

VOLCANIC RAGE

The Blackhammers besieged Mount Infernus, Khorne's greatest monument in the Seared Expanse. This was a mission of great symbolism, rather than strategy, and they cast down the mountainside as a challenge to the Blood God.

BESIEGING THE BLACK RIFT OF KLAXUS

So great was the vile ritual that took place in the Sulphur Citadel that overlooked the Kingdom of Klaxus that it ripped a passageway into the Realm of Chaos. To halt the outpouring of daemon legions from that weeping rift, Sigmar hurled down scores of thunderbolts. After days of battle, the Black Rift was finally collapsed.

LABYRINTH ASSAULT

Arriving by lightning at the Passage of Myrm, the Stormhosts found the valley realm was no more –replaced with a monster-filled crystalline maze. A dozen Stormhosts took part in that campaign, heroically led by the Hammers of Retribution.

VENGEANCE IS MINE

Four almighty monoliths had been raised over the once great city of Thal'donn, commemorating a key victory for the forces of Chaos. The Black Dracothians and Lions of Sigmar led a Stormhost coalition that levelled the region. Upon that day it was said that Sigmar smiled.

THE OPENING OF THE SKY BRIDGES

The Skyrealm – one of the twelve wonders of Ghur – had long been corrupted. Instead of assailing the fortress-laden main islands, the Stormcast Eternals struck the skybridges which connected that floating continent. Great were those battles, and much renown was won there. In the end, the skybridges were claimed only after all the Stormhosts massed their Prosecutors for a single aerial strike. However, the battle for the islands itself was far from won.

THE HELLWARRENS PURGED

The Children of the Horned Rat had spread their corruption deep in the ruined Ferruslands. Yet even the vaunted Hellwarrens – crooked strongholds formed of iron-hewn tunnels – could not stave off the Stormhosts.

THE SHIFTING KINGDOM

Manipulating a confluence of eldritch power, the Lord of Change Niz'roppxl had usurped the King's Mountain to create his own domain. Phasing between realms, this so-called Shifting Kingdom sought to spread its entropic energies to all beneath it. That campaign of conquest was halted by the Maelstrom of Light.

AZYRHEIM'S REVENGE

With many Gates of Azyr reopened, the paths into the other Mortal Realms once more lay before the vengeful armies of Azyrheim. Many war hosts issued forth, fighting on their own or aiding the Stormcast Eternals.

ALLIES JOIN THE CAUSE

As the Stormhosts descended into battle, they found many rising up to join the fight against Chaos. Some were sought-after allies, like the Iron Brotherhood; others, like the seraphon, lent unexpected aid.

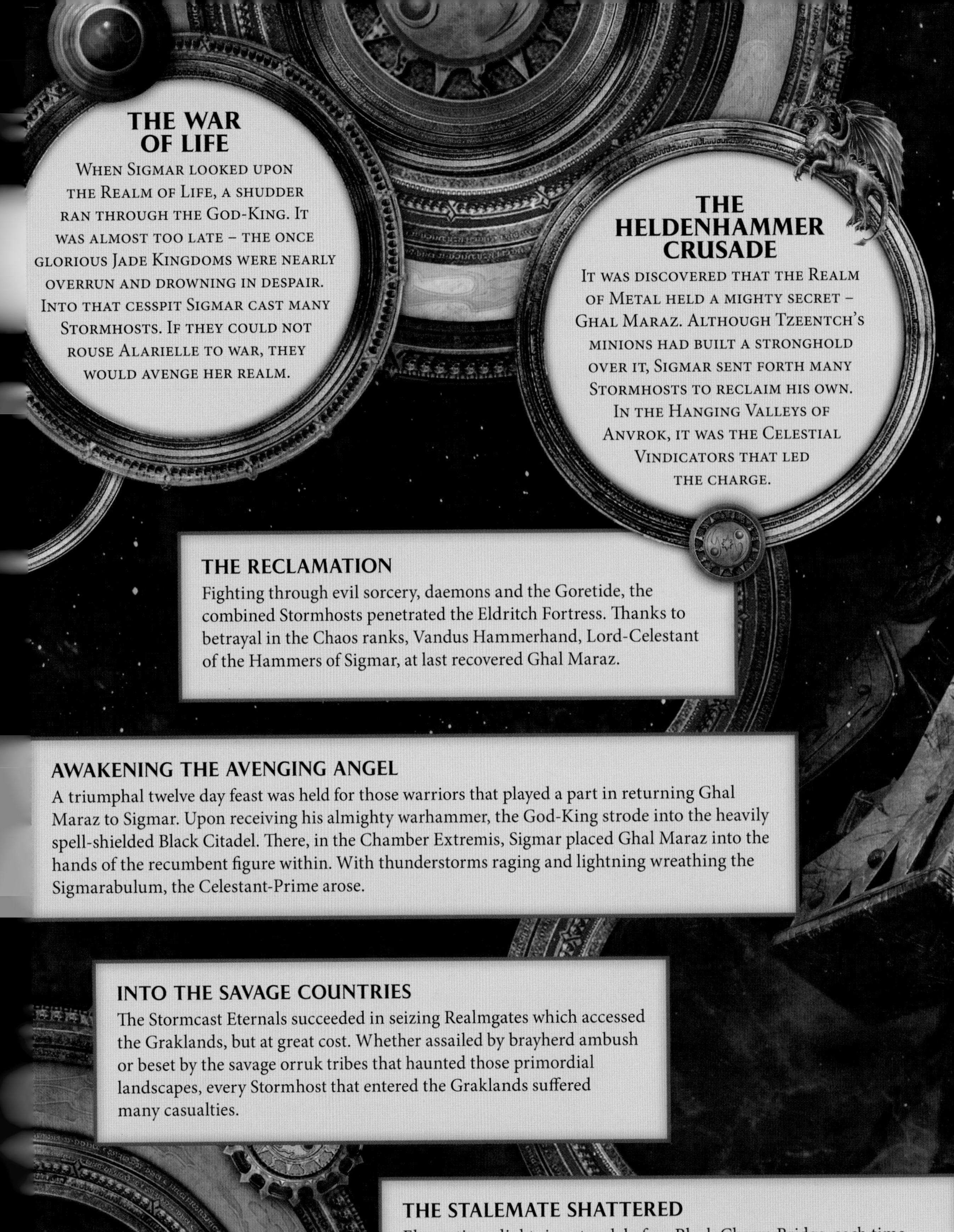

THE WAR OF LIFE

When Sigmar looked upon the Realm of Life, a shudder ran through the God-King. It was almost too late – the once glorious Jade Kingdoms were nearly overrun and drowning in despair. Into that cesspit Sigmar cast many Stormhosts. If they could not rouse Alarielle to war, they would avenge her realm.

THE HELDENHAMMER CRUSADE

It was discovered that the Realm of Metal held a mighty secret – Ghal Maraz. Although Tzeentch's minions had built a stronghold over it, Sigmar sent forth many Stormhosts to reclaim his own. In the Hanging Valleys of Anvrok, it was the Celestial Vindicators that led the charge.

THE RECLAMATION

Fighting through evil sorcery, daemons and the Goretide, the combined Stormhosts penetrated the Eldritch Fortress. Thanks to betrayal in the Chaos ranks, Vandus Hammerhand, Lord-Celestant of the Hammers of Sigmar, at last recovered Ghal Maraz.

AWAKENING THE AVENGING ANGEL

A triumphal twelve day feast was held for those warriors that played a part in returning Ghal Maraz to Sigmar. Upon receiving his almighty warhammer, the God-King strode into the heavily spell-shielded Black Citadel. There, in the Chamber Extremis, Sigmar placed Ghal Maraz into the hands of the recumbent figure within. With thunderstorms raging and lightning wreathing the Sigmarabulum, the Celestant-Prime arose.

INTO THE SAVAGE COUNTRIES

The Stormcast Eternals succeeded in seizing Realmgates which accessed the Graklands, but at great cost. Whether assailed by brayherd ambush or beset by the savage orruk tribes that haunted those primordial landscapes, every Stormhost that entered the Graklands suffered many casualties.

THE STALEMATE SHATTERED

Eleven times lightning struck before Black Chasm Bridge, each time delivering an entire chamber of Stormcasts. Eleven times were they defeated. Upon the twelfth lightning strike came the Celestant-Prime, and none could stay his wrath. Soon, the way was cleared.

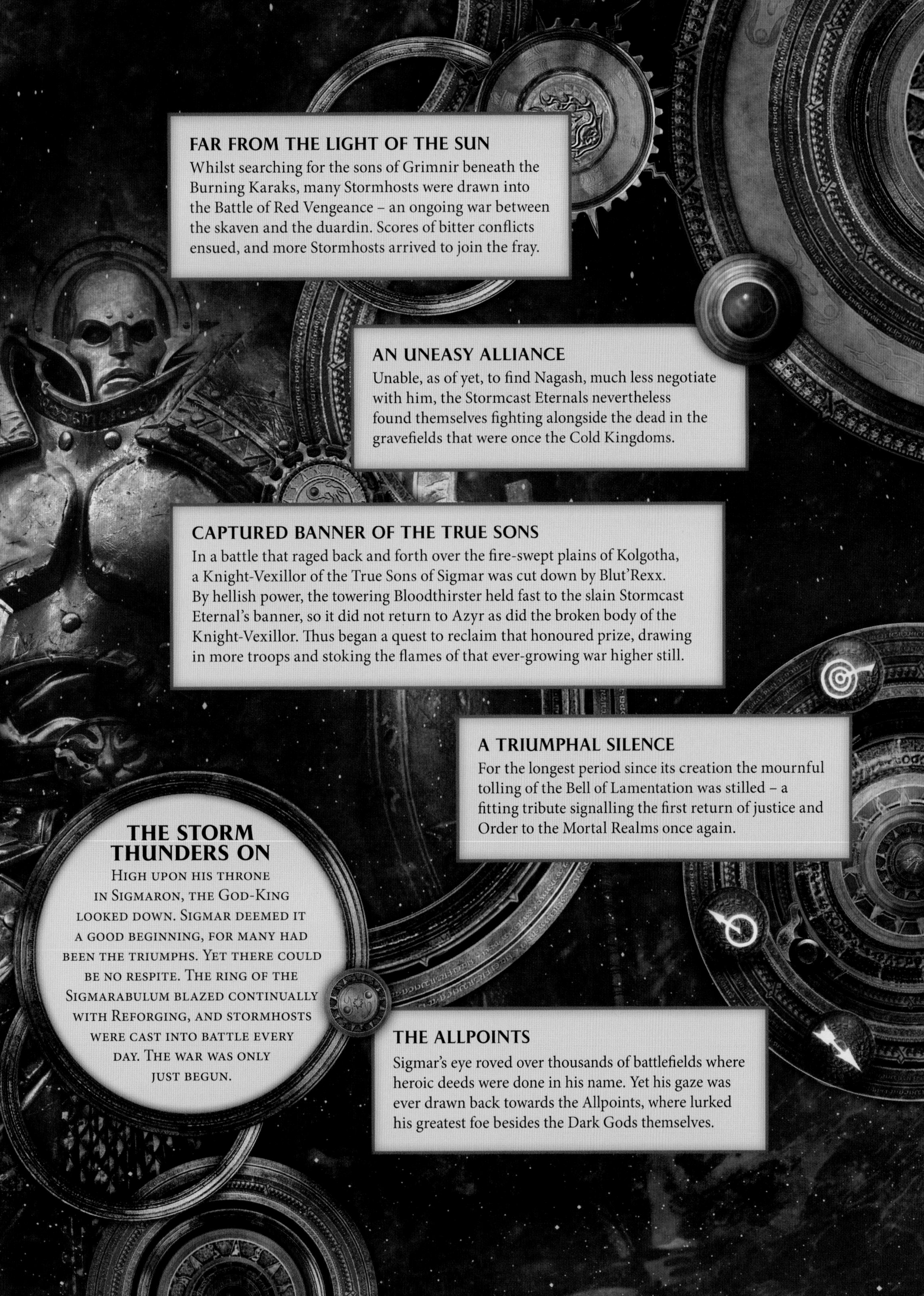

FAR FROM THE LIGHT OF THE SUN

Whilst searching for the sons of Grimnir beneath the Burning Karaks, many Stormhosts were drawn into the Battle of Red Vengeance – an ongoing war between the skaven and the duardin. Scores of bitter conflicts ensued, and more Stormhosts arrived to join the fray.

AN UNEASY ALLIANCE

Unable, as of yet, to find Nagash, much less negotiate with him, the Stormcast Eternals nevertheless found themselves fighting alongside the dead in the gravefields that were once the Cold Kingdoms.

CAPTURED BANNER OF THE TRUE SONS

In a battle that raged back and forth over the fire-swept plains of Kolgotha, a Knight-Vexillor of the True Sons of Sigmar was cut down by Blut'Rexx. By hellish power, the towering Bloodthirster held fast to the slain Stormcast Eternal's banner, so it did not return to Azyr as did the broken body of the Knight-Vexillor. Thus began a quest to reclaim that honoured prize, drawing in more troops and stoking the flames of that ever-growing war higher still.

A TRIUMPHAL SILENCE

For the longest period since its creation the mournful tolling of the Bell of Lamentation was stilled – a fitting tribute signalling the first return of justice and Order to the Mortal Realms once again.

THE STORM THUNDERS ON

High upon his throne in Sigmaron, the God-King looked down. Sigmar deemed it a good beginning, for many had been the triumphs. Yet there could be no respite. The ring of the Sigmarabulum blazed continually with Reforging, and stormhosts were cast into battle every day. The war was only just begun.

THE ALLPOINTS

Sigmar's eye roved over thousands of battlefields where heroic deeds were done in his name. Yet his gaze was ever drawn back towards the Allpoints, where lurked his greatest foe besides the Dark Gods themselves.

SIGMAR

FORCES OF THE STORMHOST

STORMHOSTS

Stormcast Eternals are organised into separate Stormhosts – each one a fighting force in its own right, hand-chosen by Sigmar for reasons and purpose only the God-King knew. Each Stormhost was unique in its forging and distinguished by its own colours and insignia.

As the power of Chaos grew across the realms, destroying or usurping all that he had tried to build, Sigmar retreated to Azyr. It was a difficult decision, for he knew well what would become of those realms and peoples he had forsaken. Yet Sigmar also realised he was fighting nought but a long battle of slow defeat. His former alliances were shattered, his armies overpowered. In losing his warhammer, Ghal Maraz, Sigmar had realised a grim truth – he must forsake the role of warrior and take up the mantle of the God-King proper. It could no longer be his task to win the battles himself, for even a god can only be in one place at a time. To triumph, Sigmar knew he must make and direct armies of defiance, that he must fashion a new kind of warrior, one that could stand face to face against the unnatural horrors of Chaos.

Thus, by godly power, arcane might and mystic machinery were the Stormcast Eternals forged. Warriors were chosen for this honour upon Sigmar's command, and organised according to his dictates. Each group was an autonomous army called a Stormhost. Each of these Stormhosts was unique in name and deed. Some were formed of warriors chosen from the same region, such as the Angels Aetheric, taken from monster-hunting tribes along the fringe of the Celestial Realm. Other Stormhosts were composed of individuals with a common trait – all of the Hallowed Knights were devout worshippers of Sigmar, warriors who had called upon their deity to aid them in battle.

BATTLE TRAINING AND FORMATIONS

A Stormcast Eternal is gifted with superhuman speed, strength and endurance, and furnished for battle with armaments made of triple-blessed sigmarite forged by the Six Smiths themselves. Yet this is not enough. Within hours of his successful Reforging, a Stormcast Eternal is subjected to tasks and training beyond the abilities of mere mortals. Such exercises are relentless, designed to hone their enhanced abilities to preternatural levels. Only when their personal martial prowess has been perfected are Stormcast Eternals allowed to train alongside their brethren. At a spoken word, the warriors pivot in unison, form interlocking shield walls or advance to lend their support and the might of their celestial energies where they are most needed by their brothers. The Stormcasts' way of war goes far beyond mere battlefield manoeuvre, as the various units support and empower each other to produce a tight-knit battle formation that moves and fights like no other army the Mortal Realms have seen before.

No one but Sigmar himself knows how many Stormhosts have been created, for Sigmaron – the sky palace that floats high above the sealed realm of Azyr – has been enshrouded in secrecy for hundreds of years. Certainly, though, the Stormhosts are built for war, each separate army organised according to a structured battle order.

Though every Stormcast Eternal is blessed with Sigmar's divine power, none are imbued so richly with godly might as the Lord-Celestants. They are chosen by the God-King himself, and are the greatest of their Stormhosts – field commanders, captains and war-leaders that can confront the greatest horrors and defeat the most powerful champions of Chaos. From them, one day, Lord-Commanders might be selected, but first these heroes must prove themselves. Beneath the Lord-Celestants in the Stormhost's hierarchy are sub-commanders, paragons of their kind that radiate Sigmar's celestial power.

Each Stormhost is divided into a number of chambers – companies comprised of different types of warrior. The Strike Chambers are the largest and make up the bulk of most Stormhosts, but each Stormhost also has additional ancillary chambers, many of which have thus far been withheld from battle for reasons known only to Sigmar himself. There are three main types of Strike Chamber, each with their own specialism – Exemplar, Harbinger and Warrior Chambers.

The exact composition of warriors within chambers can vary by Stormhost, as can the number of chambers themselves. For instance, as the heralds of the new war, the Hammers of Sigmar have more Strike Chambers than most Stormhosts, while the Celestial Vindicators field more Retributors within their Exemplar Chambers. In every case, each Stormcast Eternal is trained to fight in combination with his chamber so that the whole of the Stormhost is yet more dangerous than the sum of its individual parts.

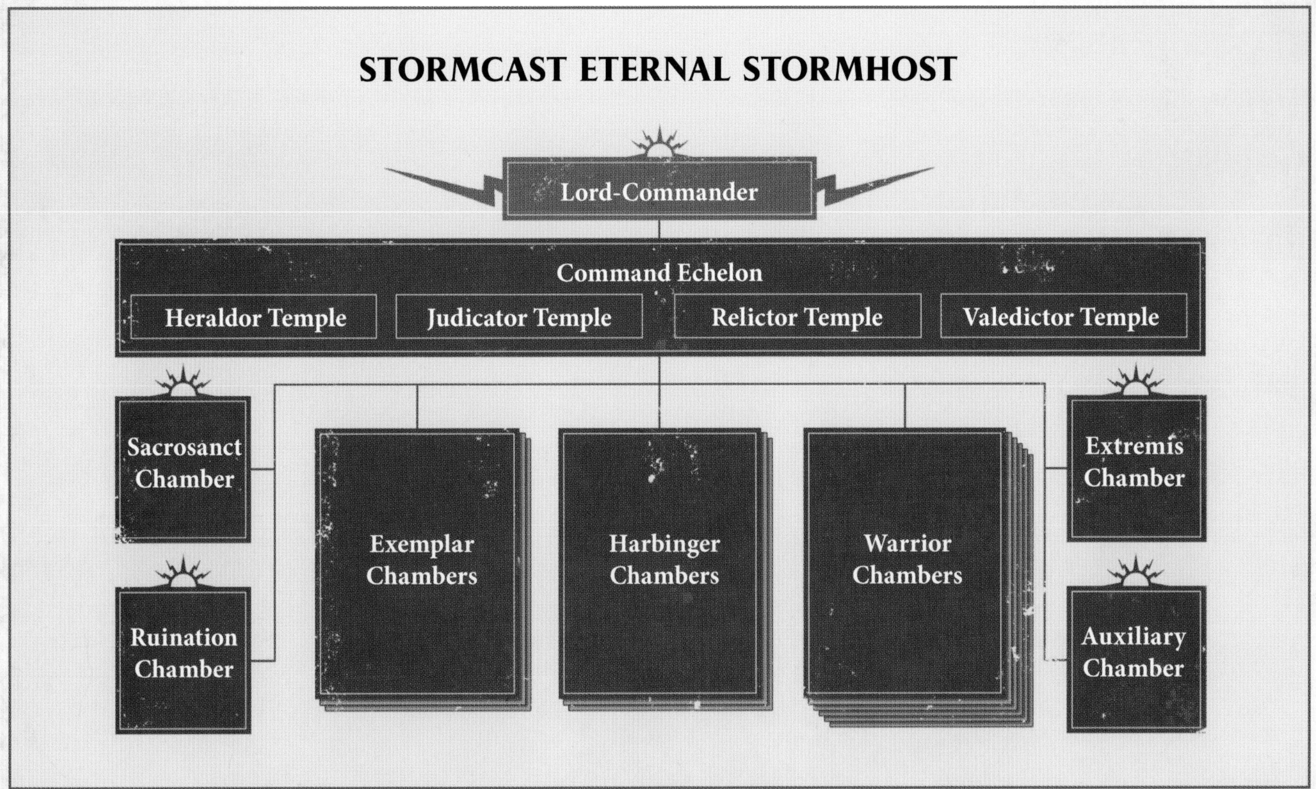

CHAMBERS OF THE STORMHOST

Each Stormhost is organised along the same general chain of command and structure. The organisation of different conclaves and retinues allows a chamber's Lord-Celestant to deploy the right troops at the right time in order to best crush his foes.

The chambers that make up each Stormhost are further divided into conclaves. All members of a conclave are armed and equipped to perform a specific battlefield role: Redeemer Conclaves contain the Stormhost's core infantry, Justicar Conclaves wield ranged death, while Paladin Conclaves are formed of hard-hitting elite units. Angelos Conclaves provide fast-striking aerial support. Under the leadership of the chamber command, the varied conclaves work together to achieve deadly battlefield harmony. The chamber command is composed of a Lord-Celestant and Lord-Relictor, and various other officers, including Lord-Castellants and Knights-Heraldor, -Vexillor, -Azyros and -Venator.

War beckons across the Mortal Realms, requiring Stormhosts to be deployed in many places simultaneously. The number of Stormcasts sent into battle is dependant upon the scale of the task – an entire Stormhost, or more, might be required to lay low a vast enemy stronghold. More frequently, however, the individual chambers that make up a Stormhost are hurled into combat, although these too can be broken down into still smaller fighting formations called brotherhoods.

As for the structure of the chambers, the Warrior Chambers are the largest, most numerous, and most tactically flexible of chambers – they form the heart of a Stormhost. The Harbinger Chambers, with their great strength of Angelos retinues, form the vanguard, relying on speed and manoeuvrability. The Exemplar Chambers are the best of the best, consisting primarily of Paladin retinues – a Stormhost's mightiest fighters. Each chamber fights autonomously, yet can combine to create a more formidable defence, or unite to power an unstoppable assault – a veritable wall of sigmarite, an army capable of toppling kingdoms.

WARRIOR CHAMBER ORGANISATION

CHAMBER COMMAND

ANGELOS CONCLAVE

3 RETINUES

Angelos retinues scout ahead of their brethren and use their mobility to harass the enemy. When battle is joined, they can redeploy swiftly to strike wherever they are most needed.

PALADIN CONCLAVE

6 RETINUES

Wherever the fighting is thickest, there are found the Paladin retinues, strongest of their chamber. Bane of terrors, each the worth of a dozen lesser warriors, there is no foe they cannot face.

REDEEMER CONCLAVE

9 RETINUES

The Redeemer retinues are the sigmarite soul of the chamber – stalwart, unflinching and relentless. The core of the Stormcast Eternals' battle line, these are Sigmar's hardiest fighters.

JUSTICAR CONCLAVE

6 RETINUES

Justicars seek out the foe's weak points, and punish them from afar with storm-forged weapons. They thin the enemy's ranks and strike at enemy commanders, for none can escape their wrath.

LORD-CELESTANT ZEPHACLEAS

To lead one of the Warrior Chambers of the Astral Templars Sigmar chose Zephacleas, and anointed him Lord-Celestant. Fearless and bold, the Astral Templars were chosen from amongst the greatest of barbaric tribal champions. In mortal life, the Stormcast Eternal who would become Zephacleas was been a giant of a man, a brawling war-chieftain of his Ghurlands tribe. They led a primitive existence, fighting off orruks and Chaos traitors alike as they travelled a nomadic path through the dense forests of those savage kingdoms. Now reforged and renamed Zephacleas, the former barbarian dwells in Sigmaron, whose shining brilliance he had once worshipped from afar as the home of the gods. The Lord-Celestant continues to lead warriors to battle, as he once did. However, his fights are no longer merely for food or tribal survival, or to clear the woods of monsters, rather Zephacleas now fights for loftier goals: the Stormcast Eternals seek nothing less than to sweep clean the Mortal Realms of the taint of Chaos.

SIGMAR

LORD-CELESTANTS

Lord-Celestants are the raging centre of each storm-strike. Thundering commands, it is they who direct the Stormcast Eternals to battle, they that lead entire chambers into the fray.

Wars can be won or lost by leadership and none know this better than Sigmar. For this reason, the God-King himself chose each of the Lord-Celestants, selecting only the best of the best – the greatest and most exceptional of mankind's heroes from across the realms. After their Reforging, they would be the field commanders and war-captains of Sigmar's new armies. Upon them, more than any others, would rest the difference between glorious triumph and bitter defeat.

Knowing well the harsh and unforgiving trials that would soon beset his Lord-Celestants, Sigmar bestowed upon each an even greater measure of his divine might. Thus did the strong grow stronger, their inherent heroism augmented by celestial energies. They became paragons of courage, duty, and martial prowess.

Lord-Celestants can bend broadswords with their hands, pulp foes with each meteoric swing of their tempestos hammers, or cut them in twain with sigmarite runeblades. Yet it is not for deeds of strength alone that Sigmar has chosen his Lord-Celestants, for it is their task to lead a Strike Chamber.

Each battle of the Stormcasts is a matter of great import. Although they are immortal, Reforging can take great lengths of time. Thus each warrior lost lessens a chamber's strength, just as each scrap of territory that remains in the hands of Chaos leaves the realms that much closer to eternal damnation. In this new war that Sigmar has launched, there are no minor losses. The Stormhosts must strike hard, and they must triumph. It is the Lord-Celestant's sacred duty to lead his forces as they seek those victories.

Dracoths are highly intelligent creatures of the celestial realm, and are sometimes taken by Lord-Celestants to serve as mounts. There are many legends told throughout Azyr about these noble reptilian beasts – their extreme loyalty and fierce disposition are renowned, and some claim they are distant descendants of the mythic Star Drakes. Dracoths are powerful beasts, their massive fangs and steel-hard claws able to tear apart the largest prey. As mystic creatures of Azyr, they have the ability to absorb celestial energies, spitting them forth as lightning – a storm-breath roar that cracks like thunder. Though they are savage creatures, once befriended they serve with tireless devotion.

LORD-RELICTORS

Lord-Relictors are high ranking commanders, second in authority only to a Lord-Celestant over a Strike Chamber. They are the Masters of Celestial Lightnings, the Storm Summoners and Bearers of the Bones of Heroes. It is they that see the spirit world, and view the soul eternal.

Lord-Relictors wield the power celestial, for they are Sigmar's priests, his lords of living lightning. Theirs is the ability to summon forth the storms of Azyr, and they use those eldritch energies either to smite the foe or to reinvigorate the bodies of their fellow Stormcast Eternals.

Across the Mortal Realms a battle rages unseen: the War of Spirits. Many opposing powers covet souls, foremost amongst them the all-consuming Chaos deities, as well as Nagash, self-proclaimed Lord of the Underworlds. In granting his new army immortality, Sigmar needed to anchor the souls of each of his Stormcast Eternals to Azyr and the divine tempest. Thus was born the role of the Lord-Relictors.

Only the most noble, most heroic of Mankind's conjurers, shamans, or prophets are chosen by Sigmar to become Lord-Relictors. Only they have the ability to incant the summonings and wield the celestial magics that will call forth the thundering aetheric powers. Yet no matter their might in the mystic arts, only those aspirants who have the deepest faith in themselves and in Sigmar survive the final test of Reforging.

Those who would become Lord-Relictors must endure the twelve rituals of the archaistic Temple of Ages. Few who enter beneath the arches of that impossibly ancient building ever return. Those that do bear the distinctive devices of their new office: mysterious relics and Mortis armour.

It is the task of a Lord-Relictor to keep the souls of his chamber's brethren firmly tethered to Sigmar and the Celestial Realm. With frequent binding rituals and lightning-wreathed blessings, Lord-Relictors ensure that should a Stormcast Eternal fall in battle, his spirit will heed only the call of Sigmar, ascending as a scintillating bolt back to the Heavens. The role of spirit-warden is but part of a Lord-Relictor's duties. He is also an advisor to his Lord-Celestant, and leads formations in his stead, or at his command. In battle, the sinister-looking Lord-Relictors channel the celestial storm, calling upon searing bolts to aid their chamber.

'Mine is the power aetheric – by the bones that I bear and call my own, I bid ye heed now, hear the Call Celestial. Heed only the call of the God-King. Godspeed to Sigmaron, godspeed back to the stars that bore ye.'

- Lord-Relictors' Incantation for the Fallen

LORD-CASTELLANTS

Lord-Castellants are the Guardians of Gateways, Keepers of Keys, and Bearers of the Warding Luminous. Each is an officer, part of the auxiliary command within a Stormhost's main chambers. Lord-Castellants are masters of defensive warfare and are often tasked with holding vital ground.

Striding the battle line, a Lord-Castellant is an indomitable force, a walking bulwark. His mere presence emboldens the fighting spirit of his battle brethren. When the powers of his warding lantern are unleashed, a mystic effect washes out with golden rays. Sigmarite plate glows as barriers of arcane protection enshroud it. Nearby Stormcast Eternals are heartened, while wounds and rents in body and armour alike are healed.

Only the most uncompromising of mortal leaders are chosen to become Lord-Castellants. Their natural tenacity is enhanced by their Reforging, creating leaders as unyielding as sigmarite. When an aspirant proves worthy of this rank, they are ceremoniously given a halberd and the sacred warding lantern. They are sent alone from Sigmaron on a final proving quest into the eternal winterlands of Azyr, the towering Boralis mountain range. There, each must prove himself by entering the madness-inducing mists that hangs over those peaks. Amidst hunting Gryph-hound packs and howling beasts he confronts the greatest fears of his former life. Only those who return from that quest can assume their new duties. These masters of defensive warfare are charged with guarding the Stormhosts' fortresses, though they are also often called upon to anchor battle lines upon the field of war.

Many Lord-Castellants march to war with a bonded Gryph-hound by their side. These incredibly loyal companions are alert guardians with eyes so keen they can penetrate any mystic veil or see through any illusion. A Gryph-hound will defend its chosen master with a fierce beak and razor-sharp claws. The Lord-Castellants too are staunch protectors – all Stormhosts maintain their own fortresses, star-scraping architectural marvels in which they house their warriors and weapons. Each Lord-Castellant is a Master of the Tower, and watches over his section of the stronghold with a noble Gryph-hound ever at his heel.

KNIGHTS-HERALDOR

When Sigmar loosed his war upon the Chaos invaders he did so with realm-shaking thunder. Out of the lightning strode his Stormhosts, and at their fore came the Knights-Heraldor. It was the clarion call of their battle-horns that announced the assault of the new armies from the Heavens.

To battle! For Sigmar! So sound the clear notes ringing from the horn of the Knight-Heraldor. Each radiant blast announces the return of justice and righteousness to the Mortal Realms. To some, the battle-horn sounds like thunder booming overhead, to others, its notes are but trumpet blasts of glory, the very sound of victory. Many hear the notes of hope returning to lands where it has been long forgotten.

A Knight-Heraldor is a Stormcast Eternal champion, an officer within the auxiliary command of a Strike Chamber. He is assigned to a brotherhood or formation by a Lord-Celestant. As a Knight-Heraldor's presence bolsters nearby comrades, they are almost always found in the midst of an assault, where the battle is fiercest. There, in the thick of combat, he exhorts his brethren to glory.

With each magnificent note sounded upon the battle-horn, a Knight-Heraldor rallies nearby Stormcast Eternals. The radiant sounds send forth a surge of celestial force, a booming wall of sound that drives and energises the just to deeds beyond normal capabilities. Each Stormhost, and indeed each different chamber, has its own specific fanfares and rallying calls.

At need, a Knight-Heraldor can turn the power of the battle-horn to destructive purposes, booming like the very voice of the God-King. These notes burst forth like a resounding detonation, a thunderclap that triumphantly announces the arrival of the armies from the Heavens. Such are the reverberations of the battle-horn that its sound can fell trees and shake buildings apart, sending them to crash down upon nearby enemies.

In combat a Knight-Heraldor is a supreme warrior, even amongst the Stormcast Eternals. Each bears a sigmarite broadsword – a blade of formidable length and heft that can be used to deadly effect. With a single flurry of powerful blows, Thullos of the Celestial Vindicators split a Khorgorath apart down the middle. Such deeds of martial prowess typify Knights-Heraldor of all Stormhosts – not for nothing is it said that where their battle-horns sound, victory follows.

KNIGHTS-VEXILLOR

Crackling with lightning and blazing with celestial energies, the banners of the Stormcast Eternals are carried proudly into battle by Knights-Vexillor. Members of a chamber's auxiliary command, these brave individuals have won the right to bear such an honoured icon of the Stormhosts.

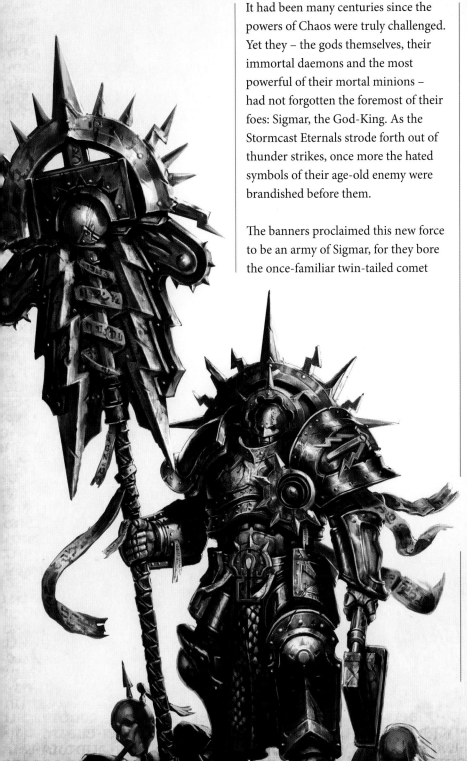

It had been many centuries since the powers of Chaos were truly challenged. Yet they – the gods themselves, their immortal daemons and the most powerful of their mortal minions – had not forgotten the foremost of their foes: Sigmar, the God-King. As the Stormcast Eternals strode forth out of thunder strikes, once more the hated symbols of their age-old enemy were brandished before them.

The banners proclaimed this new force to be an army of Sigmar, for they bore the once-familiar twin-tailed comet and hammer motifs. Yet these were not like the mundane standards of old, for they gleamed with barely contained celestial power. And the armoured figures that held the banners aloft were not mere men, but something far greater in stature. So were the Knights-Vexillor the heralds of Sigmar's Storm.

Knights-Vexillor, the champions who bear aloft the banners of the Stormhost, lead gloriously from the front. Beneath their standards can be found the Stormhost's finest, whether massed in attack formation or deployed in a defensive shield wall. Calling upon the power of his standard, a Knight-Vexillor can send forth hurricane-like tempest blasts or call down blazing stars to smite the foes.

Unlike nearly all positions within a Stormhost, the rank of Knight-Vexillor is not predetermined by Sigmar and the Reforging process. The honour of being promoted to Knight-Vexillor and carrying forth an empowered banner is earned in the Gladitorium. Entire chambers of Stormcast Eternals are pitted against each other. Although it is but mock combat, the competition is fierce, and the clash brutal. When at last a single warrior triumphs and claims the banner, he is struck by a bolt from Sigmar himself, a final charge of divine energy that courses into him and the banner alike.

KNIGHTS-AZYROS

Wherever shines the light of the Knights-Azyros, there too can almighty Sigmar see. These are the heralds and messengers of the Stormhost, the master scouts and reconnaissance leaders of the Strike Chambers. The vanguard of Sigmar's Storm, where they fly, the lightning is sure to follow...

Soaring on wings of light, a Knight-Azyros speeds across the battlefield like an avenging angel. He bears a scintillating starblade – a sword that glints and shimmers. In his other hand a Knight-Azyros carries a celestial beacon. When that lamp is unshuttered, out pours the searing light of the Heavens themselves – beams far different than the golden rays of a Lord-Castellant's warding lantern.

To those faithful to almighty Sigmar in deed and thought, the celestial beacon's beam is a wonder to behold. Flashing before their eyes are multicoloured clouds of nebulae and the shining of stars uncountable. It is but the briefest of glimpses of the all-spanning cosmos, its rays of divine illumination, the coruscating glory of all the stars that ever were. To the least of Sigmar's foes, it is something else altogether...

A scalding light. Pain heaped upon pain. Pain that grows into an agony so unbearable that death would be welcome in its stead. And they suffer but a fraction of what a minion of the Chaos powers must bear. For them – daemon or tainted mortal alike – to behold the light of the celestial beacon is a torment unlike that which even their Dark Gods could conceive. In writhing spasms of unendurable purity they twist, smoulder and dissolve into wisps of smoke, a last nothingness that is scattered by the scantest of breezes.

As part of a Strike Chamber's auxiliary command, a Knight-Azyros is deployed where his Lord-Celestant sees fit. Most often this is as the tip of the spear for a Stormhost assault, for where flies the Knight-Azyros, there also can Sigmar more easily cast his divine bolts. Knights-Azyros are messengers in the gloom of the realms, seeking out former allies and bringing light into regions where even divine Sigmar's gaze cannot penetrate.

KNIGHTS-VENATOR

The Knight-Venator is a sky-archer, a winged hunter that glides over the battlefield raining death upon the foes of Sigmar. With a screeching Star-eagle flying by his side, this celestial knight can streak out of nowhere, quickly take aim, and bring down even the largest or most powerful of enemies.

Almost before a man can blink a Knight-Venator can nock and loose not one arrow, but an entire volley of shots. The hunter's actions are a blur – only faint glowing contrails and the whirring hiss of arrows in flight give away that any shots have been fired at all. That is, of course, until the missiles find their mark. A Knight-Venator is not only incredibly quick when he strikes, but also deadly accurate. Armed with a realmhunter's bow, he can put three arrows through a helmet's visor from a great distance, before the target has time to lift hand or shield in defence.

A Knight-Venator is a Stormcast Eternal champion – a member of a Strike Chamber's auxiliary command. Each Knight-Venator is a deadly asset, deployed to lead Prosecutor retinues, or given individual assignments to target specific enemy leaders or monsters. In the role of hunting assassin, these warriors are unmatched. They can speed into position and strike from afar, quickly firing off a series of deadly volleys to pincushion their target. Those rapid shots can pitch a Chaos Lord off his bestial mount or take the eye from a charging Cygor.

The arrows a Knight-Venator carries are magical in nature, as are the quivers they bear them in. Made by the Six Smiths, each quiver fills as quickly as the shots can be loosed. However, there is one missile of especial note – the Star-fated Arrow. Forged of comet-struck steel, this triple-blessed arrow is so powerful it takes many hours to rematerialise in the quiver. When shot it leaves behind a bright, iridescent trail and strikes like a clap of thunder. Against powerful targets, the Star-fated Arrow crashes into its target with extra potency, so that a single shot can topple a hulking Aleguzzler Gargant or fell a mighty Lord of Plagues.

During training exercises, Knights-Venator scour the celestial space – launching themselves from the Sigmarabulum that rings the Broken World. It is during these hunts that each Knight-Venator finds and bonds with the fierce raptors known as Star-eagles. These creatures hunt the Aetheric Clouds, their eyes able to see the ethereal and their claws able to rend such creatures, ripping them into reality as they tear their flesh apart.

LIBERATORS

At the core of the Stormhosts stand the Liberators – the armoured foot soldiers of Sigmar. In perfect lockstep they march out of lightning strikes, eager to begin their vengeful war against the forces of Chaos. Before their unified front, even the largest and most powerful of foes must fall.

Liberators are the most common type of soldier amongst the Stormhosts. In mortal life each was a hero of mankind – a warrior chosen by Sigmar for their martial prowess, great strength or the steel within their souls. Blasted apart by lightnings, they are reforged anew, physically and spiritually blended with gifts from the gods and the God-King's blessing. Now near bursting with celestial energies, these are the main strength of Sigmar's new armies.

Every aspect of the Liberators is shaped by the needs of Sigmar's war. Clad in armour of sigmarite, they are armed with a range of celestial-forged weapons. The battles of the Cleansing and incessant drilling developed the Liberator retinues from a collection of individuals into perfect fighting units. As one they now march, turn, and raise nigh impenetrable shield walls. After learning to fight as a unit, the Liberators train in larger formations.

All Stormcast Eternals are imbued with a portion of the God-King's might, but some, like the Paladin conclaves, are so thundercharged with mystic power that other nearby Stormcast Eternals can draw upon and make use of their energies. As part of their training exercises, Liberators learn to channel this power, making their force even stronger than the sum of its component retinues.

During their training, natural leaders emerge. Sigmar himself summons these warriors before his almighty presence. They are further blessed with divine powers and sent back to serve as retinue-level leaders, known as Liberator-Primes.

When Sigmar unleashed his Stormhosts upon the mortal realms at last, Liberator retinues poured out of the lightning strikes. With warhammers they battered down the foe, with warblades they pierced them. Inexorably the Liberators march over those who oppose them. As one they are intent on laying low the tyrant, on breaking the dominion of the fiend, on casting down the oppressor. Each burns with the celestial fires that course alongside the blood in his veins. Each Liberator is eager to smite the foe and to reclaim the lands in the name of justice, Order, and their liege, almighty Sigmar.

JUDICATORS

A Judicator can always see the taint of Chaos, discerning its foul presence even if no physical corruption is present. To see Chaos is to judge it, and by decree of Sigmar himself, there is but one resolution. In a swift motion, Judicators aim and fire, sending forth bolts of instant justice.

Theirs is the power of death from afar. Armed with skybolt bows or boltstorm crossbows, retinues of Judicators scour swathes of the battlefield by loosing hails of deadly missiles fire.

Skybolt bows send forth arrows that in flight turn to arcs of lightning. Upon reaching their target, the sparkling bolts strike with such force they can easily penetrate armour or the toughest of hides. Boltstorm crossbows, though shorter-ranged than skybolt bows, fire much at a much greater rate. They shoot out a flurry of bolts, crackling shafts of energy that can fell multiple foes in a single volley.

Judicator retinues can most often be found fighting alongside Liberators, for they both form a major part of the Warrior Chambers of any Stormhost. In small numbers Judicators provide supporting firepower, while in larger retinues they can eradicate entire enemy attacks themselves, dropping rank after rank of charging foes before any assault presses home. Should a foe prove numerous enough to withstand such an onslaught and actually reach the Judicators' lines, they will find no easy mark. When each warrior draws his storm gladius – a short, stabbing sword – the Judicators can more than hold their own in combat.

Some Judicator retinues provide heavier support in the form of a shockbolt bow or thunderbolt crossbow. A shot from a shockbolt bow explodes into a writhing chain of lightning that can scorch a series of targets or immolate a single unfortunate foe. The hefty thunderbolt crossbow instead fires a twin-tailed comet of energy which strikes with deadly and explosive impact.

Thus far, of all the Stormhosts, the Sunbolts have made the most use of massed Judicator retinues. Such has been their success, however, that many other Stormhosts will soon follow suit.

RETRIBUTORS

The Retributors are the Storm that Walks, the wrath of the Heavens made manifest. Each Retributor bears a lightning hammer, a massive weapon around which celestial energies fizzle and spit. The justice they bring might be slow to arrive, but when it does so, it hits with thunderclap power.

With each swing of their mauling lightning hammers, the Retributors add to the growing tales of their sheer power. They can be found where the battle is at its fiercest, wading forward, swinging their mighty hammers in wide arcs. Such is the force and shock of their blows that broken shards of shields, armour, or bone fly upwards as the Retributors plough their way deep into enemy lines.

So great is the weight of their lightning hammers that it would take six mortal men to lift one of the two-handed weapons, but the impact of a perfectly landed strike from one of these hammers results in more than just a crushing blow. A resounding clap of thunder rolls as the hammer blow releases a dazzling flash of crackling sky-magic, blasting the target apart. Such a blow can splinter stone or explode a foe in a shower of burnt gore. Working in unison, their hammers rising and falling as one, a Retributor retinue can batter and break down the most towering of beasts. Even greater daemons would be wise to hesitate before approaching within reach of those energy-laden hammers.

Retributor retinues are formed from Paladins, the elite heavy infantry of the Stormhosts. They can be found in great numbers in a Stormhost's Exemplar Chambers, although some retinues can also be found within its Warrior Chambers as well. They are shock troops ideally suited to assault, and some Stormhosts – such as the Celestial Vindicators and the Astral Knights – feature more retinues of Retributors than of any other type of Paladin. The Blackhammers, too, favour Retributors, for their brand of heavy, bludgeoning destruction is ideal for casting down the fell idols of the Dark Gods.

Some Retributors bear a starsoul mace rather than a lightning hammer. The shockwaves from these weighty weapons tear souls from broken bodies, felling waves of incoming enemies at once. The ability to slay multiple foes with every swing makes for a deadly addition to a Retributor retinue.

MARELLUS LIONHEART, RETRIBUTOR-PRIME

A stalwart champion of the Leonus tribe, the mortal that would be reforged as Marellus Lionheart had never before lost a personal combat. Many times he had stood before the hulking fiends of the invading Bloodcall Horde, felling foes larger than himself. Looking down from on high, Sigmar recognised a hero of mankind, yet the God-King had knew how such a tale would end. It was only a matter of time before the mortal's luck would expire, and he would be pitted against a warrior gifted with more unnatural power than even the greatest of humanity's fighters could confront and live. So did a bolt split the skies, taking that champion, snatching him from battle. After his Reforging, he was renamed Marellus Lionheart, a Retributor of the Hammers of Sigmar. It was in the Gladitorium battles that Marellus won the title of Retributor-Prime, for he wielded a lightning hammer with a deftness that belied the colossal weight of its impact. With steadfast courage Marellus led his retinue to greatness in battle, splattering foes with every strike.

PROTECTORS

They are the Masters of the Mystic Stormshield, the Guardian Paladins. With their martial skill and the arcane ability of their stormstrike glaives, Protectors lend aid to nearby retinues. Yet their abilities extend beyond defence, for these warriors are elite shock infantry, able to confront any foe.

As they whirl, the stormstrike glaives of the Protectors weave patterns of celestial energies that shimmer and hang in briefly visible contrails behind the blurred blades. So powerful is this mystic aura that it forms a partial shield, a deflective force capable of blunting arrows and mystic bolts alike. In this way, Protectors earn their namesake, shielding the retinues behind them with their own armoured forms, as well as with the arcane veil woven by their glowing weapons.

Assembled from the ranks of Paladins, Protector retinues frequently spearhead an assault. The heavy shock infantry can not only clear a path with sweeping blows of their stormstrike glaives, but the storm-shield they weave before them can also offer protection to the formations that follow. It is for this reason that they are often the foremost of the Stormcast Eternals to stride forth from a lightning strike or Realmgate.

On the battlefield, Protectors frequently form a bodyguard around Lord-Celestants or Lord-Relictors, although it is not unheard of for them to perform the same function for any of the auxiliary command. These formations plunge fearlessly into combat, cleaving a bloody path for others to follow.

During the Battle of Durek's Drift in the highlands of Chamon, the skaven levelled all of their insidious weaponry at the two Hammers of Sigmar chambers that attempted to ascend the steep pathways. With faith in Sigmar, sturdy sigmarite armour, and several retinues of Protectors in the vanguard, the Stormcast Eternals advanced step after step. Straight into the teeth of that hellish firepower they went, enemy shots ricocheting everywhere. When they finally reached the battle line of their mangy foes, the Protectors led the victorious charge. Stormstrike glaives sliced holes into the swarms of ratmen, scything them down with every swing.

DECIMATORS

The Decimators are the Destroyer Paladins, the Axemen of Azyr. Enemy hordes slough away into twitching gore beneath the onslaught of a Decimator retinue. With thunderaxes whirling side by side in well-trained harmony, Decimators can quickly annihilate hundreds of foes with a deadly efficiency.

Decimators plunge deep into enemy formations, driving all before them. Armed with the formidable thunderaxe, a lone Decimator can slay half a dozen lesser foes with each great sweep of his blade. A retinue of these Paladins can carve a gore-ridden path straight through an attacking foe's lines. Even when they are buried beneath heaving tides of the enemy, it is possible to mark the Decimators' progress. Where they fight, severed limbs and decapitated heads are flung skywards with each axe swipe, and many foes flee rather than face such destruction.

Decimators are more than able to triumph against powerful foes, such as Sourbreath Troggoths or Blood Warriors, but it is against enemy hordes where the broad sweeps of their deadly axes reap the greatest harvest. Swarming skaven, green tides of orruks, or droves of lesser foes have all been cut down like so much wheat before the scythe.

All Stormhosts boast retinues of Decimators, but some, like the Sons of Mallus and the Helden Sons, favour them above all other Paladin retinues. No Decimators have earned more fame thus far than those of the Astral Templars. It was in the Gnarlwood of Ghur that four chambers of the Astral Templars were ambushed, encircled by beastmen and hulking monsters beyond count. Five sorties were led to break out of the ever-closing encirclement, yet all met with failure. Only when the Decimators massed together did the Stormcasts make any headway. The Decimator formation hacked a bloody pathway through the enemy – felling beast-foes and treegrowth alike. At last, by following in the Decimators' wake, the Astral Templars fought their way to freedom.

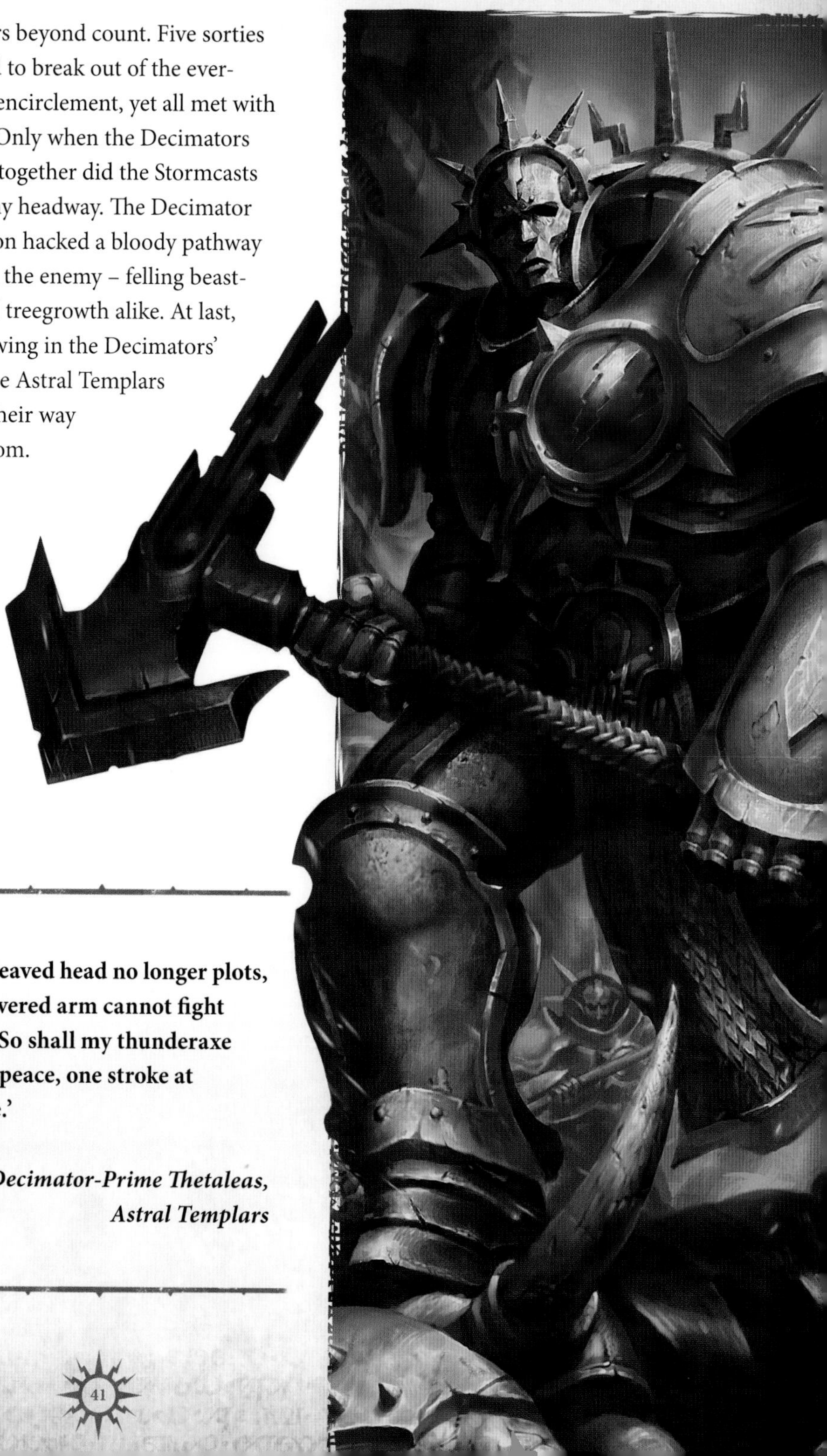

'The cleaved head no longer plots, the severed arm cannot fight back. So shall my thunderaxe make peace, one stroke at a time.'

- Decimator-Prime Thetaleas,
Astral Templars

PROSECUTORS

Prosecutors are the warrior-heralds of Sigmar, and the message they bear is one of violence and retribution. Soaring upon blazing wings, they hurtle across the battlefield in a blur of shining sigmarite, hurling down celestial hammers or stormcall javelins before swooping to the attack.

Gliding out of the storm come the Prosecutors, glowing like avenging angels. Their wings gleam in resplendent rays, like the brilliant light from some nearby star. As if from the tempest itself they summon weapons, hammers or javelins materialising in their outstretched hands. These lightning-wreathed weapons can be hurled down into the foe from range – never unarmed, the Prosecutors simply gesture and another weapon manifests in a blaze of light. A perfectly hurled stormcall javelin channels a thunderbolt, calling the strike onto itself. In combat, the weapons radiate a glowing nimbus of power.

The celestial hammers were wrought by the Six Smiths out of pure celestial energies and are summoned at need.

Prosecutors are the most common of the Angelos retinues, and can be found in all three of the main Strike Chambers, making up a large portion of the Harbinger Chambers in particular. In battle, they use their speed and manoeuvrability to outflank the foe, hurling their deadly weapons and then plunging down to finish them.

Although they soar through the air, the Prosecutors work alongside those on the ground – wheeling above them in support or darting over them to launch their own lightning attacks. They are often at the tip of the celestial spear-strike, their vengeance inescapable.

Beaten, whipped and chained, the enslaved workers shuffled in an unbroken line that stretched beyond the horizon of the flatplains. Those who tried to flee were subjected to torments so horrific that being worked to death seemed preferable. And then, with no warning whatsoever, it happened.

The twelve suns of high noon that blazed over this burning land were blotted out. Into that blackness came a searing bolt, blinding all even as the thunderclap brought them to their knees. Where that lightning had struck stood an army, their shining armour glowing and resplendent, still crackling with sparks of energy. None had seen their like before, and the enslaved cowered in terror. Yet not so the Blood Ravagers, or their spike-armoured leaders. They howled at this new challenge, breaking ranks to lope towards the foe.

Even the Bloodstokers halted their incessant whipping, staring opened-mouthed at this gleaming warhost. On a tempest's wind, more arrived. They soared upon wings that radiated starlight – armoured angels that bore thunderbolts in each hand. Hurricane-swift they swooped, striking again and again before streaking skywards once more. In one fluid motion the foot soldiers locked into a shield wall against which the ravagers clanged in vain, failing to break through. In return, the hammer blows of these warriors rang like thunder. They did not merely break bones, but crushed the ravagers, splattering them in blazing bursts. None could stay the wrath of the golden newcomers, and they reaped a terrible slaughter, slaying mercilessly until no follower of Chaos remained. Torn between awe and terror, the enslaved fled as more storms darkened the horizon. A new age had begun.

THE CELESTANT-PRIME

The Celestant-Prime is nothing less than the Storm of Sigmar itself. Those who meet the Celestant-Prime in battle face firsthand the full brunt of the God-King's wrath, for he is the Avenging Angel of Azyr, the Bearer of the World-Hammer, and the First Scion of Sigmar.

He was the most heroic of mankind's champions, a great king and guardian of men from an age rapidly growing darker. When he was chosen as the first by Sigmar, the God-King poured into him a prodigious portion of divine might. Yet the process was not fully concluded – this greatest of aspirants remained in stasis in the storm-wracked dome of the Forbidden Vault. Without Sigmar's hammer, Ghal Maraz, the first Stormcast was incomplete.

When the Stormcast Eternals at last reunited Sigmar with Ghal Maraz, the Celestant-Prime arose, shimmering and resplendent. In that moment thunder rolled across the realms – its intensity shaking skulls from the foundation of the Brass Throne. In the most brilliant of bolts the first of the Stormcast Eternals joined Sigmar's armies on blazing wings, his gleaming armour flickering with chains of lightning, always appearing to match that of the Stormhost he was fighting alongside. With each arcing hammer swing, the Celestant-Prime smote the wicked, the bludgeoning force sweeping away ranks of oncoming foes at a time.

Full of the energies of the Celestial Realm, the Celestant-Prime's hammer blows can slay a greater daemon with a single thunder-cracking impact, breaking its body, and banishing it utterly. Yet such is the power of the Celestant-Prime that there is yet more than sheer destruction within those mighty concussions. If there is the slightest kernel of uncorrupted soul left in the smitten, then the blow frees the spirit even as it crushes the tainted form. Those who are redeemable are purified. Spirits loosed in such a manner are not dragged into the Realm of Chaos, nor do they dissolve into the Underworlds ruled by Nagash. Instead, the spirits wing their way to Azyr, there to be presented before almighty Sigmar. The final judgement is his, and his alone, for a place in his armies awaits the few who are found worthy.

Thus did Sigmar's new War against Chaos bring the corrupting ways of the Dark Gods back full circle.

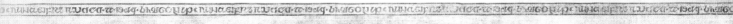

GHAL MARAZ, THE GREAT SHATTERER

Ghal Maraz, the Skull Splitter, comes from the mythic ages that predate the awakening of the realms. It is a great weapon of war and trails a twin-tailed comet when swung with sufficient force. Grungni himself mined the starmetal of which Ghal Maraz was forged. Struck with runes of justice, the hammer is bane to Chaos, and only the most powerful of the Dark Gods' minions can bear to look upon its radiant nimbus. As legends tell, Sigmar first used his hammer to raise mankind from barbaric squalor, wielding its might to unite a kingdom. Foes untold have fallen beneath its mauling blows, and while wielding Ghal Maraz Sigmar was never bested in combat. Yet during the Battle of Burning Skies illusionary magics – and his own impetuous rage – tricked Sigmar into hurling Ghal Maraz into the void, where it was lost for many centuries. Now, at last, the warhammer has been returned to Sigmar, who in turn has passed it on to his greatest champion.

HAMMERS OF SIGMAR

Let all who would oppose order and justice be warned – the Hammers of Sigmar have been unleashed. They are the power and majesty of the tempest, the fury of the bolt from the heavens made manifest.

The first Stormhost to be founded, the Hammers of Sigmar are the forerunners of the celestial storm. Gleaming and resplendent in their golden armour, they bore the honour of being the Stormcast Eternals sent into battle to strike the first blow of Sigmar's new war on the Brimstone Peninsula. Since that initial blow, the Hammers of Sigmar have carried forth their proud banners into all the Mortal Realms. Bold, daring, and utterly committed to bringing down furious vengeance upon the Chaos oppressors, or any who dare oppose the God-King's justice, the Hammers of Sigmar will ever be found at the forefront of the battle to reclaim the realms.

HAMMERS OF SIGMAR

As the first Stormhost to be founded, the Hammers of Sigmar are true heralds of the God-King's new war. They are exemplars in deed, as well as in their military order, and in their use of heraldic markings and insignia. Theirs is the glory of Azyr and the power of the storm.

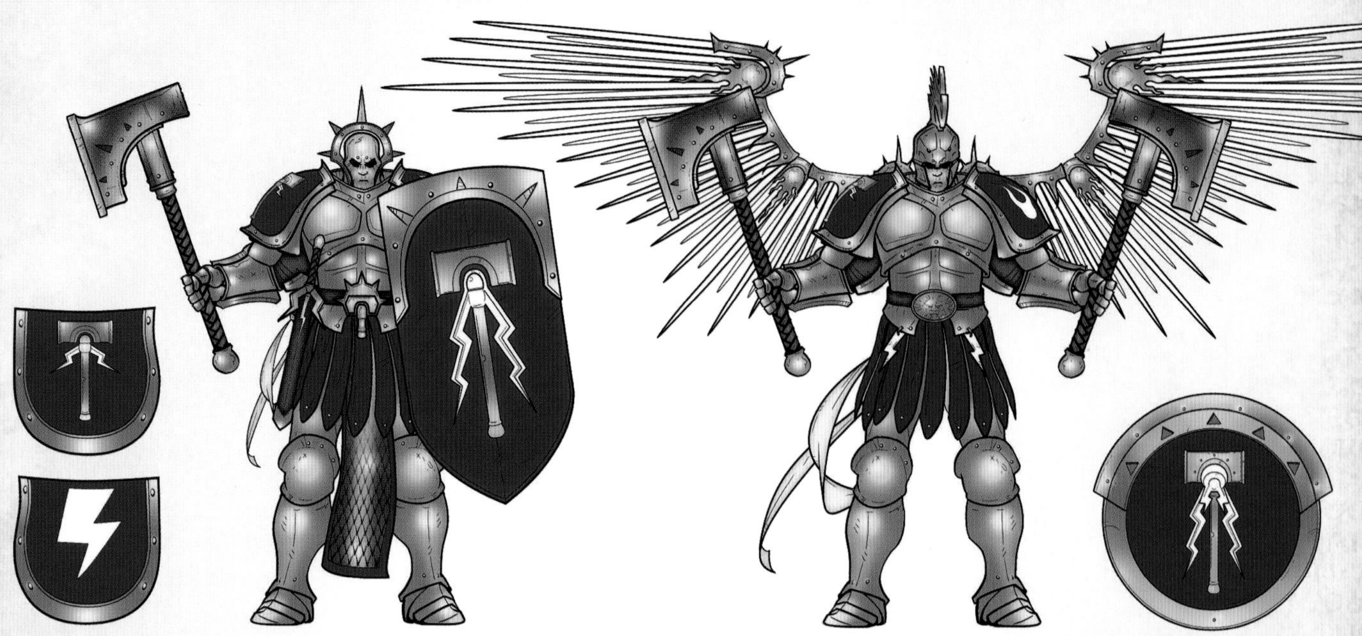

Stormhosts are designated by different colour schemes. The colours of the Hammers of Sigmar are the gleaming gold of sigmarite and the sky blue of Azyr.

All the varied warriors of the Hammers of Sigmar bear their Stormhost's colours, as does this Prosecutor. The crest's colour declares which chamber a warrior serves.

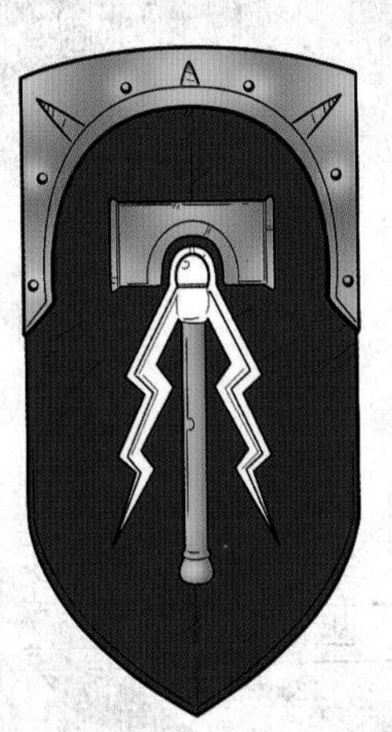

SHIELD DEVICES

The shields borne by warriors from the Hammers of Sigmar display the lightning bolts of Sigmar's storm, accompanied by a golden hammer. Several meanings are attached to this all-important iconography; the hammer represents both the Stormcast Eternals – who were created through the Reforging process – and also Ghal Maraz, the fabled hammer wielded by Sigmar himself in the Age of Myth. The twin-tailed comet refers to the tale of how Sigmar entered Azyr, and is the predominant symbol of the God-King. The lightning bolts also glorify the sudden strike that delivers the Stormcast Eternals from Azyr into the heart of combat.

CHAMBER DESIGNATION

Many Stormhosts, including the Hammers of Sigmar, identify their chambers by the colours of their plumes or crests. Each type of retinue has a distinct helm design; in some retinues, all the warriors wear the colour of their chamber, while in others only the Prime wears a plume. The chamber's colour is picked by their Lord-Celestant – the Hammerhands display red plumes.

SHOULDER ICONOGRAPHY

The icon borne on a Stormcast's left shoulder denotes that warrior's battlefield role. The lightning bolt represents the Redeemer Conclaves, the twin-tailed comet identifies the Angelos Conclaves, the crescent moon – found on their right shoulders – is for Paladin Conclaves, and the star is for the Justicar Conclaves.

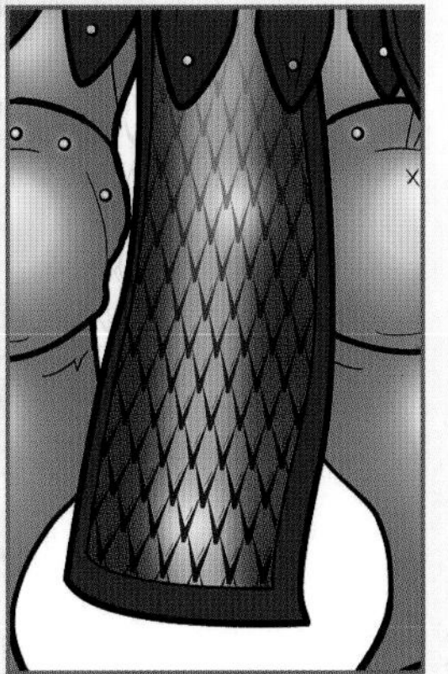

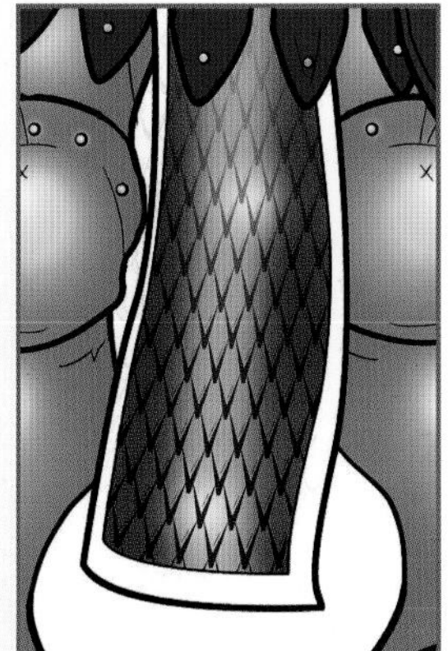

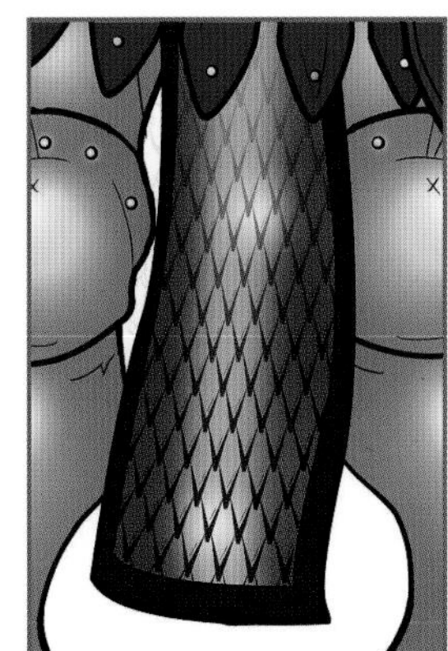

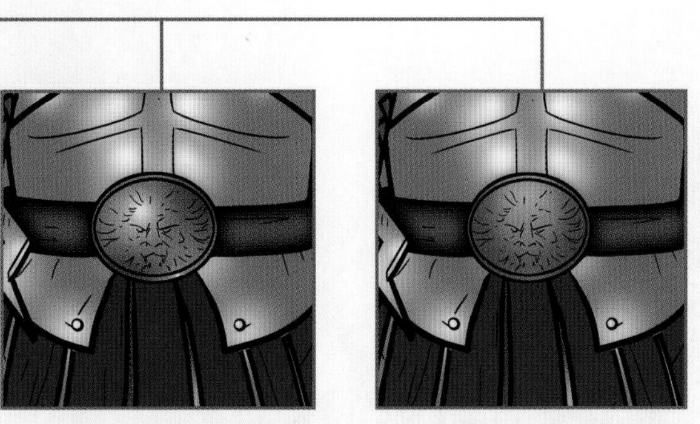

TABARDS & BUCKLES

Within each of a chamber's conclaves can be found a number of different retinues. Each individual retinue within a chamber is identified by the colour of the trim around the tabard, although there can be up to three retinues with the same trim colour. When this is the case, each of these is further distinguished from each other by the colour of their buckles – gold, silver, or bronze.

In the Hammers of Sigmar, the same pattern is used for all of the conclaves, so that a combination of colours can be repeated several times in a chamber. For example, there is a retinue of Liberators, a retinue of Judicators, and one of Retributors all with blue-trimmed tabards and gold buckles.

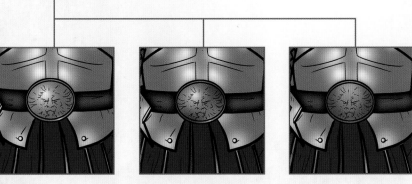

A Judicator armed with a skybolt bow. The star on his shoulder marks him as part of a Justicar Conclave.

This Judicator-Prime is part of the Hammerhands Chamber, as indicated by his red plume.

This Judicator carries a boltstorm crossbow. His retinue all wear gold buckles and a white tabard trim.

This Liberator-Prime's black plume identifies the chamber his retinue belongs to. Like many Primes, he also wears an ornamented shoulder plate honouring his rank.

This Liberator is armed with a pair of warhammers. He is part of a retinue marked by white trim and silver buckles, and bears a Redeemer's lightning bolt on his shoulders.

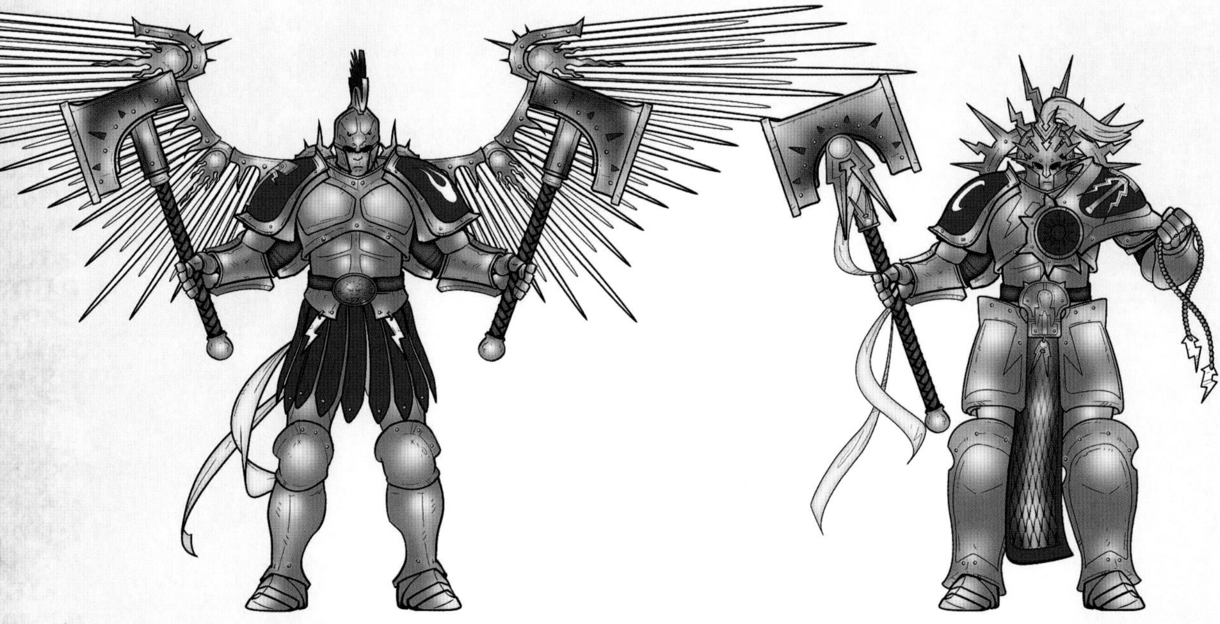

The black crest upon this Prosecutor's helm marks the warrior as part of the Stormbound Warrior Chamber. The silver buckle indicates which retinue he belongs to.

This Retributor-Prime hails from the Starfall Exemplar Chamber, who wear white crests at their lord's command. All his retinue bear the same trim and buckles.

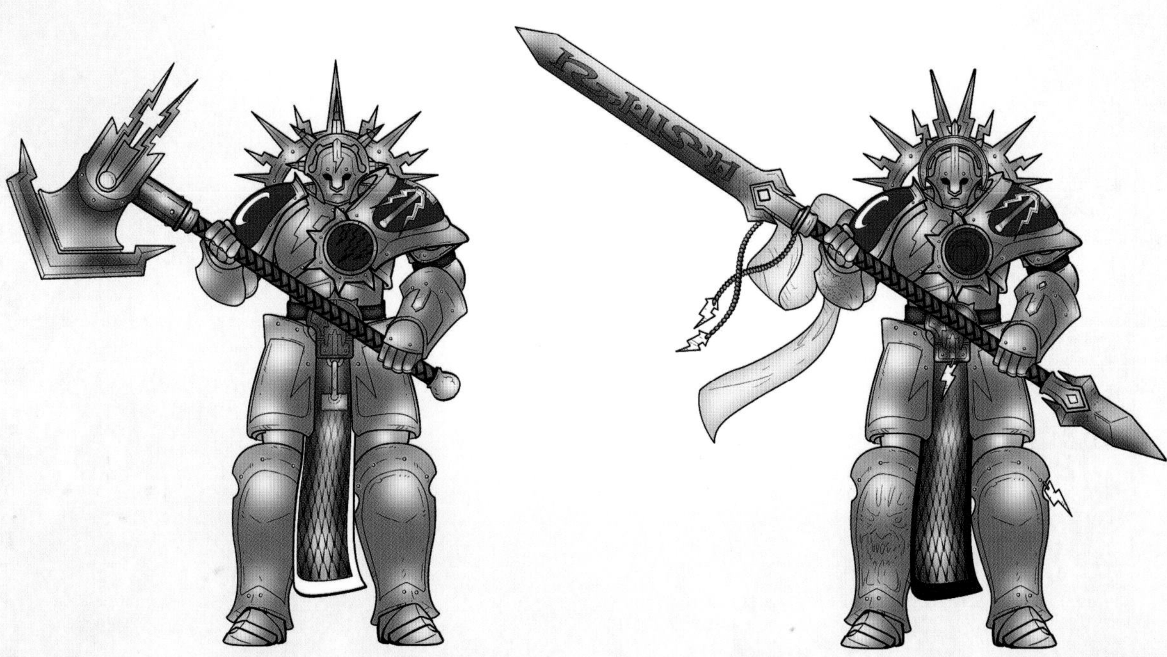

Decimators are part of the Paladin Conclaves, as indicated by the crescent moon on their right shoulders, and bear deadly thunderaxes to battle.

Protectors are also part of the Paladin Conclaves and are armed with stormstrike glaives. Silver buckles and black tabard trim distinguish this Protector-Prime's retinue.

HALLOWED KNIGHTS

There is no sacrifice too great for the Hallowed Knights, for they are a Stormhost that live to serve Sigmar. 'Only the faithful' is their warcry – and they shout it out repeatedly as they relentlessly smite their foes. The ranks of the Hallowed Knights have been filled exclusively with mortal warriors who worshipped Sigmar and called his name while fighting heroically for a just cause. They did not receive the divine aid for which they beseeched, but rather were taken into the Heavens. There, in vision resplendent, the God-King himself spoke to them of the service they might render unto him. Only those who embraced this weighty commitment survived their soul-scouring Reforging. No matter the cost, no matter the casualties, the Hallowed Knights will see the battle won or die in the attempt.

HALLOWED KNIGHTS

The fourth Stormhost to be founded, the Hallowed Knights are Sigmar's rock – unquestioningly loyal, zealously faithful. The war against Chaos is to them a holy crusade, a sacred mission. The Hallowed Knights are a powerful blend of matchless martial might combined with unshakable fealty.

The burnished silver of the Hallowed Knights represents their untarnished souls, the blue of their shoulder guards Azyr, whilst the red of their tassets stands for sacrifice.

Here is seen a Prosecutor bearing the colours of the Hallowed Knights. The gold belt buckle denotes which retinue the warrior belongs to.

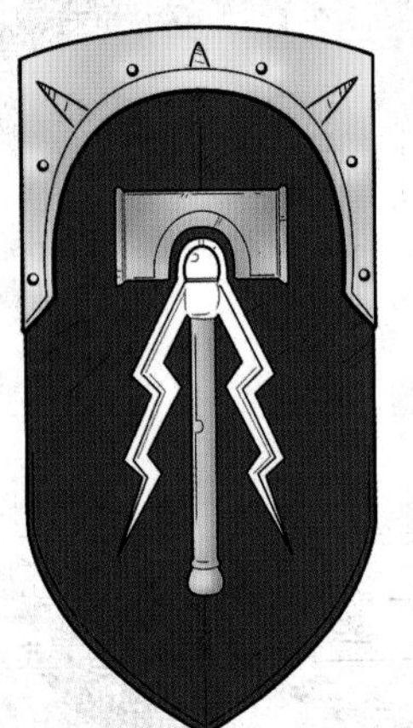

SHIELDS OF THE FAITHFUL

As worshippers of Sigmar, the Hallowed Knights put great meaning into the symbolism they bear upon their wargear. To the Hallowed Knights, the hammer-and-lightning symbols they wear upon their pauldrons and shields represent the Helden Stars, the divine constellation that shines upon divine Sigmar and lends strength to his followers. The lightning can also symbolise not only Sigmarabulus, the twin-tailed comet that blazoned Sigmar's birth, but also the awesome power of the storms themselves.

CHAMBER DESIGNATION

Like many other Stormhosts, the Hallowed Knights use the colour of the crests and plumes that bedeck their warhelms to distinguish the warriors of different chambers. Shown here are the plume colours for the Steel Souls, the Stormforged and the Purehearts, Warrior Chambers of the Hallowed Knights.

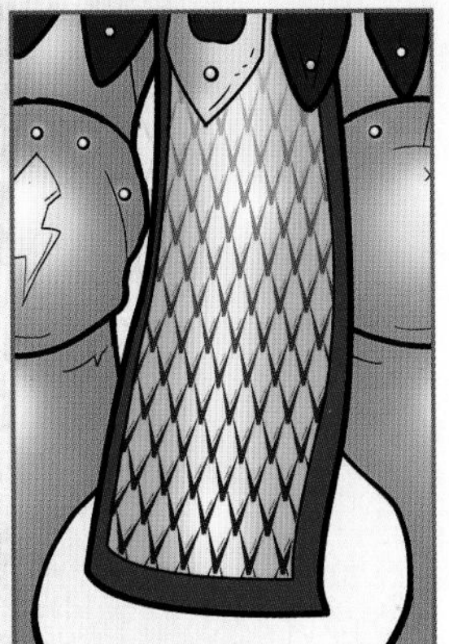

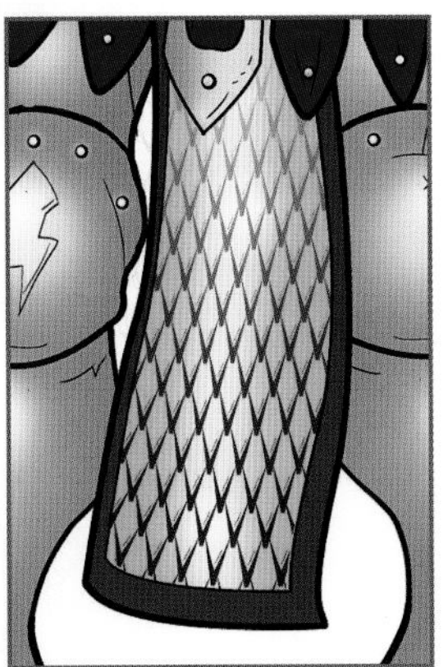

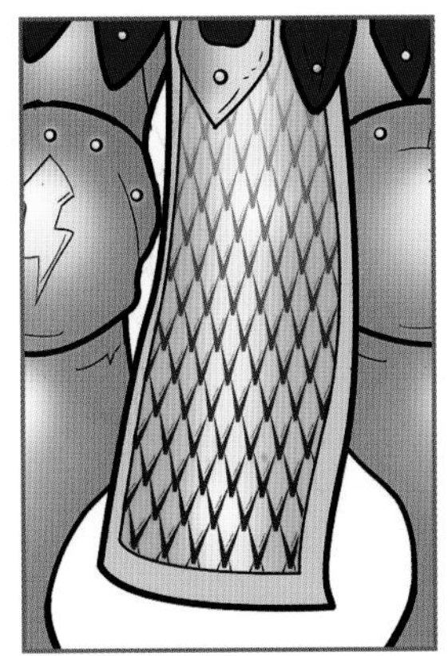

RETINUE MARKINGS

The Hallowed Knights use blue, red or cream trim upon tabards of gold to mark out which squad each warrior belongs with. Up to three retinues may bear the same colour, but they are further distinguished by gold, silver or bronze belt buckles. All of the chambers in the Stormhost follow this same pattern of unit recognition.

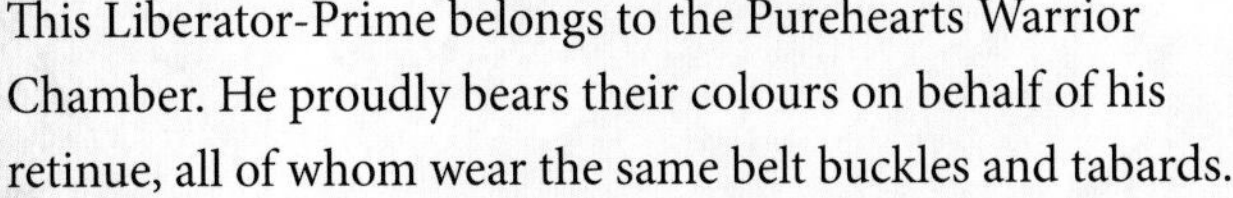

This Liberator-Prime belongs to the Purehearts Warrior Chamber. He proudly bears their colours on behalf of his retinue, all of whom wear the same belt buckles and tabards.

This Hallowed Knight Liberator carries a warhammer and a sigmarite shield. The red trim upon his tabard and the bronze belt buckle will be worn by all in his retinue.

CELESTIAL VINDICATORS

Fierce and fell-handed, the warriors of the Celestial Vindicators are as unforgiving as they are unrelenting.

Only those mortal heroes that have suffered great loss at the bloody hands of Chaos forces are considered to become Celestial Vindicators. Yet there is a grimmer requirement as well. To be selected, the mortal warrior, whether chieftain or youngling, must ask Sigmar not for aid or salvation, but rather for the might to reap his own vengeance. Moreover, an aspirant must be covered in the blood of a worthy Chaos foe – a champion, daemon or great beast. These are dark conditions, but the Age of Chaos was a dark time.

On the fields of battle, the war songs of the Celestial Vindicators are terrifying to hear – for these warriors exult in their reaping and stay focussed by chanting a mantra of terrible vows of vengeance.

CELESTIAL VINDICATORS

Stern and single-minded are the sixth of the Stormhosts, for vows of vengeance have they spoken, forming hate-bonds with their comrades. In battle, they contain their fury with grim chants and warsongs, yet they prefer most of all to let their hammers speak for them...

There is no mistaking the turquoise armour of the Celestial Vindicators. Like all the Vanguard Stormhosts, they bear the hammer symbol on their right shoulder pad.

Alongside their turquoise armour plate, the Celestial Vindicators bear gold sigmarite trim, red accoutrements, and tabards of silvercloth.

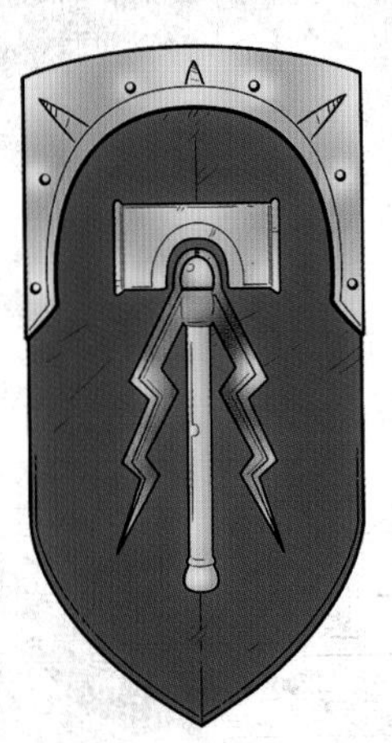

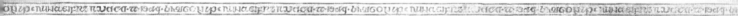

SHIELD DEVICES

Celestial Vindicators bear shields of gold-trimmed turquoise. The iconography borne by these sturdy devices is typical of all Vanguard Stormhosts – those created in the First Striking. The symbols reference their liege-lord and deity Sigmar, including lightning bolts, Ghal Maraz – which they refer to as the Hammer of Righteous Smiting – and the blazing comet. Sometimes, Liberators of the Celestial Vindicators add scrolls to their shields or even inscribe intricate runework on the inside of these bulwarks. These runes spell out fiercely worded vows of vengeance and verses which the warriors can chant in the maelstrom of battle to focus their fury.

CHAMBER DESIGNATION

The colour of the crest or plume signifies to which chamber a warrior belongs. Liberator-Primes wear the colour for their entire retinue. Of the Celestial Vindicators Warrior Chambers, purple is the colour for the Bladestorm, black is the colour for the Swiftslayers and white is for the Wrathsworn.

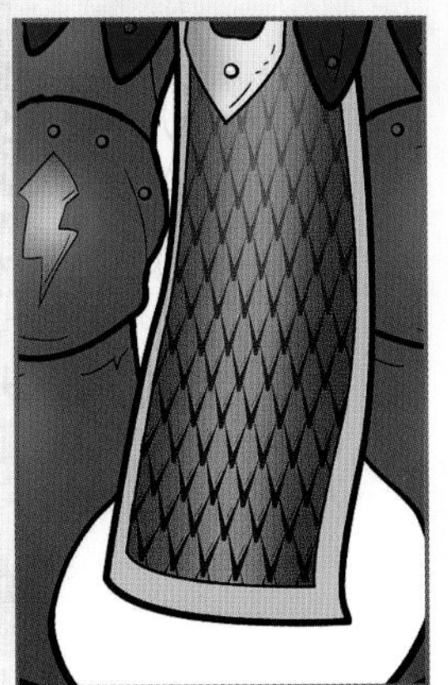
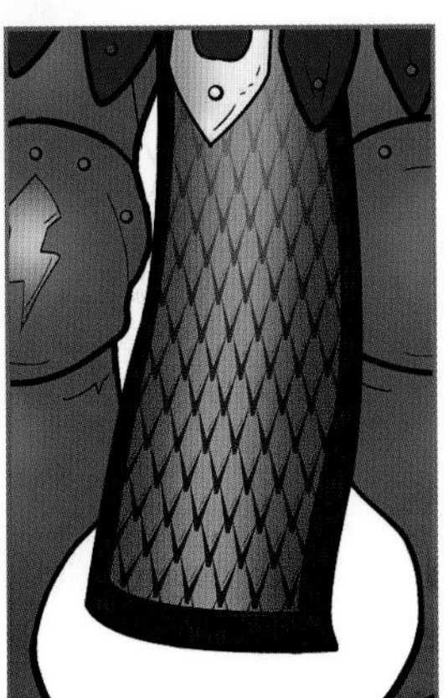
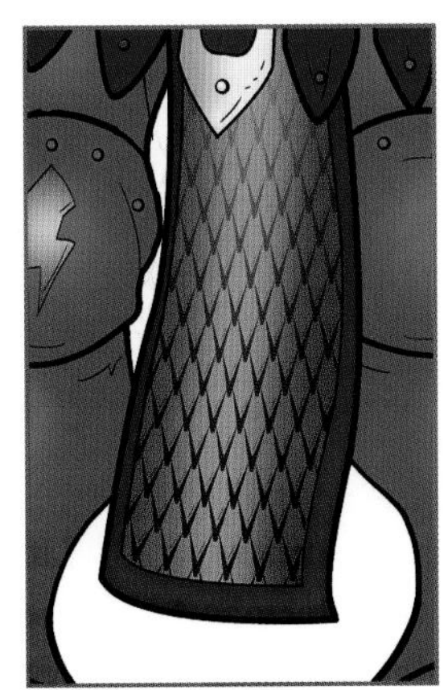

TABARDS

The tabards of the Celestial Vindicators are made of finely wrought silvercloth mined in the mountains of Azyr. The combination of the trim around the tabard and the colour of the belt buckle indicates which retinue a warrior belongs to. All of the chambers in the Celestial Vindicators use these colours.

SHOULDER ICONS

The Celestial Vindicators use symbols upon a white field on their left shoulder to signify their conclave. Lightning is for Redeemers, the twin-tailed comet for Angelos, the star for Justicars, and the crescent moon – on the right shoulder – for Paladins.

MIGHTY WAS THE TEMPEST

Long he forged them, strong he made them. In lightning strikes were they cast down into battle unending. How many Stormhosts were created only almighty Sigmar knows, yet each will be needed to reclaim the realms from Chaos. Featured below are but a selection of those the God-King first struck.

The dark blue of the Celestial Knights is reminiscent of the gloaming skies of Azyr at twilight, yet this Stormhost crusade to bring the light of Sigmar to benighted lands.

Little is known of the mysterious Lions of Sigmar, save for their heraldry and the thunderous roar of their battle cry, yet Chaos has tasted their wrath in many of the realms.

The Sigmarite Brotherhood were recruited from Chamon, the Realm of Metal. None can stand before their relentless advance of their exemplary shield walls.

Their measures extreme, their methods merciless, the Astral Templars seek to purify the lands of all Chaos. None may stay their wrath.

A sinister Stormhost, the Anvils of the Heldenhammer were reforged as the Broken World spun under a phase of fell magic. They are grim of aspect.

No Stormcast Eternals strike more quickly than do the Knights of the Aurora. As swift as lightning bolts, they are masters of rapid assault.

There is no Stormhost more proud than the Blades of Dawn. They are composed of champions taken from the riftcoast tribes of many different realms.

The Maelstrom of Light are daemon-killers supreme. In Ghur, it was they that turned back the daemon legions at the Battle of Verdant Abyss.

THEY WHO RIDE THE THUNDER

Before Sigmar could launch his new war, he needed to build an army vast and powerful. For hundreds of years the God-King laboured, halting only to fight the Battle of Stars, of which many mythic tales are told. After that triumph, Sigmar returned to his task, creating further strikings of Stormhosts.

The Knights Excelsior bring to battle with them crackling chains of celestial lightnings. 'For the Glory of Sigmar!' is their motto.

The Sons of Mallus were forge-struck under the zenith of the darksome span of Dharroth, the Dark Moon. Their armour is a lustrous black.

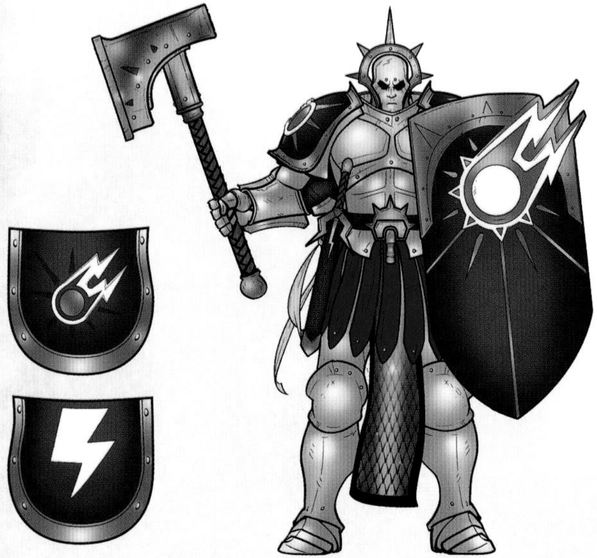

Named after a fierce raptor of Azyr, the Lightning Hawks strike out of blue skies. They are the scourge of Chaos and bane of daemons.

In battle the Radiant Suns of Sigmar gleam with the brilliance of Sigendil, the High Star. Theirs is the purity of justice, the might of the righteous.

The Sons of the Storm crash upon their foes in a deluge of violence. In common with many Second Striking Stormhosts, they bear the icon of the hammer and bolts.

The Ghyran Guard were formed from a single tribe of warriors, the last of their kind. They reserve a special hatred for the minions of Nurgle.

The Celestial Warbringers were the first Stormhost of the Second Striking. They bear the sign of the twin-tailed comet as their symbol.

For boldness and surety of action none can best the Fists of Sigmarite. It is their vow to be first in glory, and they seek hammer-worthy deeds.

CALL OF THUNDER

The Knight-Vexillor and Knight-Heraldor can be found fighting in the thick of the fray.

Like the sun's rays bursting through storm clouds, Prosecutors streak down upon the foe.

A Lord-Celestant leads a Liberator retinue to war – with all the fury of a thunderstorm, none shall escape their justice.

The Stormcast Eternal battle line stiffens beneath the glowing radiance of a Lord-Castellant's warding lantern.

The Celestial Vindicators break enemy battlelines with the thundershock force of their attack

With powerful sweeps of their thunderaxes, a Decimator retinue leads the assault.

Lord-Castellant

Knight-Heraldor

Lord-Celestant, Hammers of Sigmar

Lord-Relictor

Knight-Vexillor with meteoric standard

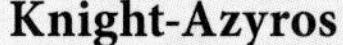

Knight-Azyros

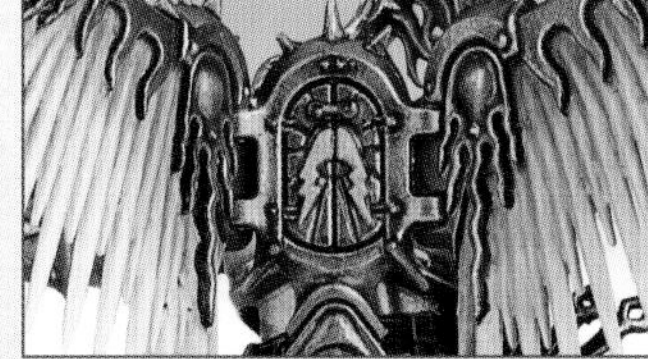

Knight-Venator, Hammers of Sigmar

Retributor with lightning hammer

Decimator-Prime

Protector with starsoul mace

Protector, Hammers of Sigmar

Liberator-Prime

Prosecutor with celestial hammers

Prosecutor, Anvils of the Heldenhammer

Judicator with thunderbolt crossbow

Liberator with grandblade

Liberator-Prime, Celestial Warbringers

Judicator, Lions of Sigmar

Liberator-Prime, Celestial Vindicators

Liberator with paired warblades

Prosecutor, Astral Templars

Judicator with boltstorm crossbow

THE WAR OF VENGEANCE

THE REALMGATE WARS

When Sigmar retreated to the Celestial Realm, he shut tight the Gates of Azyr. The first test of the God-King's new armies would come when they attempted to reopen those long-sealed portals, regaining easy access to the embattled realms. So began the Realmgate Wars.

Save for the most powerful masters of the eldritch arts, the only way to travel between realms was by Realmgates. These mystic portals allowed a traveller to bridge vast gulfs of unnavigable paths, to traverse otherwise impossible distances.

Since the ascendancy of the Age of Chaos, none had passed through the Gates of Azyr. All Realmgates that led into the Celestial Realm had been shut, sealed tight by enchanted wards. Many besieging armies had battered those gates, monsters and hell-forged daemon engines alike pounding upon them, yet still the gates stood firm.

While Azyr remained safe, the other realms suffered wave after wave of crushing Chaos invasions. By seizing the Realmgates, the minions of the Dark Gods separated and broke apart the last remnants of Sigmar's pantheon and the civilisations that had thrived underneath their rule. One by one these kingdoms fell. The domination of the Chaos powers was so complete that rival factions fell to fighting amongst themselves over the spoils of victory.

As long as the mystic wards protecting Azyr were in place, the inhabitants were safe, but Sigmar would not be able to deploy the full might of his armies – the gates could only be reopened by forces working on both sides. Before Sigmar could reveal his true strength, Realmgates would have to be seized. For this task, Thunderstrike Brotherhoods led the way, opening routes so further Stormcast phalanxes could march through the open gates.

The Stormcast Eternal assaults upon the Gates of Azyr were wholly unexpected. An azure mist had long shrouded Azyr, keeping secret Sigmar's resplendent new armies. The shock of those assaults was indescribable – the sheer audacity of their defiance reverberated even in the Realm of Chaos.

There the beast stood, filling the arch of the Realmgate with its immensity. As it roared out its challenge, the air shimmered from the sheer heat of its unbound hate. The creature was the stuff of nightmare. Blood dripped from its muzzle, already turning to red steam upon the glowing metal of its impossibly broad-bladed axe. Gore dripped from the spikes of its cruelly barbed whip. No man could will his body to approach such a hulking fiend, for it reeked of charnel houses and bore the aura of slaughter untold. Indeed, only the greatest of champions could dare, even for a moment, to meet the iron intensity of that monstrosity's ferocity-filled gaze. Even the merest glance was open challenge to the Bloodthirster Khorg'tan, the Living Rage – vassal of Khorne's immeasurable power, incarnation of but a shattered shard of the Blood God's unbearable fury.

Yet Lord-Celestant Mordaus was no man, nor were any of his heavily armoured Retributor guard. For a moment Mordaus sat in the saddle of his Dracoth, staring, all emotion hidden by his armoured mask.

Sensing a challenger, Khorg'tan turned to face the Stormcast Eternals and bellowed a harsh furnace roar. Shadowed reflections flickered across the armour of the Celestial Vindicators as they gazed up at the towering greater daemon. The hellish creature seemed to grow larger in its fury, its every move a promise of pure violence. Its whip cracked, splitting stone.

Without a word, Lord-Celestant Mordaus urged his mount forward, and the Dracoth clawed its way over the piles of crumpled bodies littering the ground. Slow at first, it soon gained speed. Behind the charging Dracoth came the Retributor guard, hammers held high.

Like a hurtling comet, Mordaus charged into the shadow beneath Khorg'tan's outspread wings, the impact of the ensuing clash echoing across the battlefield. The berserk frenzy of the blood-maddened daemon was matched by the cold might of celestial vengeance. Here were champions made for battle, warring for supremacy – lightning-wreathed hammer versus bloody axe. Only one would survive that day.

IN FIRE WERE THEY PROVEN

Sigmar's lightning bolts struck across the oppressed realms, and the shock of those initial attacks began a new legend. The very first blow was landed in the Realm of Fire, where the Hammers of Sigmar, soon reinforced by a dozen other Stormhosts, wrought their long-awaited vengeance.

To begin his great war in Aqshy, Sigmar chose scores of initial targets. Most were Realmgates, closed portals that once led back to the realm of Azyr.

To lead the way on these crucial assaults, the God-King chose the first of his Stormhosts, the Hammers of Sigmar. They would not fight alone. Brotherhoods from other Stormhosts joined the fray, and soon the whole Brimstone Peninsula blazed. There fought warriors from the Lions of Sigmar and the Anvils of the Heldenhammer, as well as vanguard elements of other Stormhosts. The foe would do anything to defend that region, for it was rife with portals, and accessed many realms.

As important as the capture of the Brimstone Peninsula was, there were many other bolts cast forth to secure equally vital targets in Aqshy and elsewhere. From out of blue skies came peals of thunder, and lightning streaks that smote the ground. Thus was the Ironpassage, a Realmgate leading to Chamon, assailed. So too was the Scintillating Portal, a pathway that led to the realm of Ghyran. The last bolt to strike in Aqshy delivered Stormcast Eternals to besiege great Mount Infernus, the largest volcano of the triple-ringed Vulcanus Range.

Back in Sigmaron, amongst the stars that hung above the realm of Azyr, those Stormhosts held back for future strikes stood ready. Rank upon rank were mustered, gathered in the celestine vaults, awaiting the call to battle. All knew that everything depended upon those first cast. If those initial strikes failed, then so too would Sigmar's plans. Even with the surprise of those shock attacks on their side, the Stormcast Eternals sent in the first wave would soon be overwhelmed, ground down and buried by counter-attacks. The minions of the Dark Gods were numerous beyond sanity, and, although they had been made to combat them, as of yet, the Stormcast Eternals had never been tested against them.

In those tense hours it was as if all of Sigmaron held its breath.

LORD-CELESTANT VANDUS HAMMERHAND

All Stormcast Eternals are heroes – great champions of mankind further gifted with divine powers and weapons beyond the ken of mortals. It is none other than Sigmar himself who selects the leaders of each Stormhost – his far-seeing eye able to penetrate a man's spirit. The God-King saw in Vendell Blackfist a young tribesman burning with a desire for vengeance like few others. It is said that none passed through the Reforging process more quickly than did he. Renamed Vandus Hammerhand, Sigmar saw in him great things and anointed him a Lord-Celestant of the Hammers of Sigmar – the first founded of his new Stormhosts. During the wars of the Cleansing of Azyr, Vandus proved himself time and again – earning a Dracoth mount, the blessed hammer Heldensen, and the respect of his warrior comrades. Such was the supreme confidence Sigmar placed in Vandus that he and the Stormcast Eternals he commanded were chosen as the lead element – the tip of the spear – in the crucial first wave of attacks that would begin the Realmgate Wars.

Though each of the brotherhoods sent to Aqshy had its own mission, it was Vandus Hammerhand, Lord-Celestant of the Hammers of Sigmar, who faced the greatest challenge. He was sent to oppose the leader of the Goretide, Korghos Khul, the very same warrior who had long ago destroyed his tribe. Indeed, had Sigmar not whisked the mortal from the battlefield, Khul would have surely slain him before he could be reforged into a Stormcast Eternal.

In a series of fierce battles, the Hammers of Sigmar fought through the Goretide, at last forcing open the Realmgate. This victory reverberated high above Azyr, and Sigmaron flashed in the Heavens. Down Sigmar cast his armies, sending bolt after bolt of Stormcast Eternals, while more still poured forth from the newly opened Realmgate. The Igneous Delta blazed with war as Stormhosts met the Chaos counter-attack head on.

In the midst of that onslaught, Vandus duelled Khul, pitting sacred hammer against daemon-forged axe. The Lord-Celestant, recognising the killer of his former tribe, overcame his nemesis, and smote him into the mud with the hammer Heldensen. However, the tides of battle swept them apart before Vandus could strike the killing blow. Through a vision, Vandus came to a grim realisation – Khul had corrupted a nearby Realmgate.This yawning red portal now served as a channel for the fell power of Khorne. Unless it could be destroyed quickly, the Stormhosts would be ground down upon the Brimstone Peninsula, prevented from expanding their war and bringing justice to other lands in Aqshy.

Even while the Hammers of Sigmar led other Stormhosts to close this Gate of Wrath, they were simultaneously attempting to defend the Gate of Azyr from the resurgent Goretide. The Lions of Sigmar, resplendent in heraldic purple and gold, had surged north to draw off the westernmost hordes of Khul's Bloodbound warbands, while to the east fought the Stormhost of the Anvils of the Heldenhammer.

Many Stormcast Eternals fell as they held the Goretide back from joining the fight. Noble and valorous of deed, they gave their lives in sacrifice to bear the brunt of the attack from the Wrathmonger tribes.

The stalwart Lord-Castellant Andricus Stoneheart held firm against the tide of blood-crazed warriors that assailed the Gate of Azyr. Yet his heroic defence would be for naught, if the steady flow of daemons from the Realm of Chaos could not soon be halted.

Having fought their way past spiked brass towers, the Hammers of Sigmar at last besieged the Red Pyramid, a horrifying skull-mountain raised in praise of the Blood God. There, before the Gate of Wrath, Vandus once more met his archfoe in combat. They traded blows that would each have felled dozens of lesser warriors, yet neither could end the fight. At last, in desperation, Vandus called upon Sigmar himself, summoning forth a bolt from the heavens. The detonation of that celestial lightning sundered the archway to the beyond, Vandus' sacrifice sealing shut that baleful portal.

Elsewhere in the lands of Aqshy, the Ironpassage too had been secured. The Bloodthirster Khorg'tan, the Living Rage, halted the first two Stormcast Eternal strikes at the Scintillating Portal, but fell to the relentless blows of the Celestial Vindicators. Hard fighting won a dozen other Realmgates, allowing for the passage of massed Stormhosts into Aqshy. Even the battle at the great Mount Infernus was winding down, though there were no mortal eyes there to witness it. Continents away from the Brimstone Peninsula, amidst fiery desolation, the Blackhammers had fought against daemon legions, pitting the fuel of their vengeful redemption against raw fury.

Once the Vulcanus Range had been home to a mighty empire, the most formidable in Aqshy. Now, those flame-spewing mountains were but sacrificial pits in which skulls were offered to Khorne. As slaughter washed across the lands, their once majestic shape had warped so that they looked like a leering skull – its sockets glowing with magma as the grim monument gazed out over dismal lands. Targeting the Realmgates had been tactical, but the decision to send the Blackhammers to level the largest monument to Khorne was purely symbolic.

'Let them shake in their rage, for our war is just and our vengeance only begun.'

- Lord-Celestant Vandus, Hammers of Sigmar

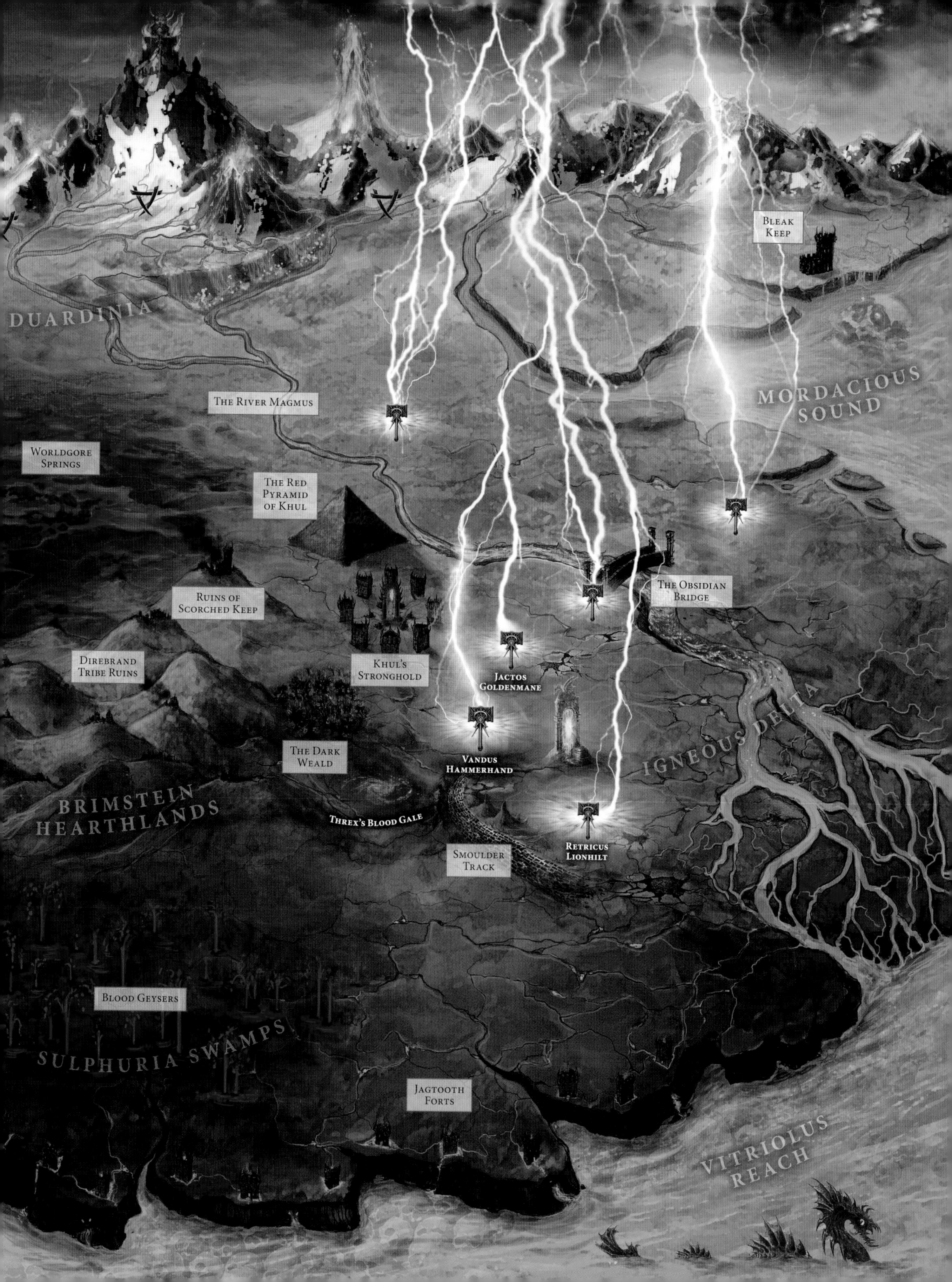

Duardinia
The River Magmus
Bleak Keep
Mordacious Sound
Worldgore Springs
The Red Pyramid of Khul
Ruins of Scorched Keep
The Obsidian Bridge
Direbrand Tribe Ruins
Khul's Stronghold
Jactos Goldenmane
The Dark Weald
Vandus Hammerhand
Igneous Delta
Brimstein Hearthlands
Threx's Blood Gale
Smoulder Track
Retricus Lionhilt
Blood Geysers
Sulphuria Swamps
Jagtooth Forts
Vitriolus Reach

LIGHTNING STRIKES

HOW TO USE BATTLEPLANS

This book contains three battleplans, each of which enables you to fight a battle based upon the exciting narrative that leads up to it. These battles should be fought using all of the rules on the *Warhammer: Age of Sigmar* rules sheet unless the battleplan specifically indicates otherwise. Each of the battleplans includes a map reflecting the landscape on which the battle was fought; these maps usually show a battlefield that is 6 feet by 4 feet in size, but you can use a smaller or larger area if you wish.

Sigmar's Storm has broken at last, and Lord Vandus Hammerhand and his warriors are the first to bring vengeance to the forces of Chaos. As battle began on the Igneous Delta, strikes landed across the realms to retake Realmgates. This battleplan lets you recreate the explosive arrival of the Hammers of Sigmar, or any similar conflict in which the Stormcasts attempt to claim a Realmgate that is held by the enemy.

THE ARMIES

One player commands the Stormcast army, and the other represents the custodian of the Realmgate.

The general of each army has a unique command ability, shown below, in addition to any others they have.

STORMCASTS' OBJECTIVES

The time has come for the Stormcasts to make their first move. You will strike deep into the enemy's heartland and reclaim a long-lost Realmgate. If possible, you must achieve absolute command of the battlefield by wiping out the enemy threat in the area; however, if the enemy numbers are too great, you must secure the Realmgate at all costs and hold it against any enemy counter-attack.

CUSTODIAN'S OBJECTIVES

In a stunning and audacious move, the Stormcast Eternals have launched a rapid assault upon a Realmgate under your stewardship. To lose control of such an important site would not only be humiliating, but could hamper your war effort for years to come. Victory will only be yours by scouring the battlefield; leave none alive to threaten your control of this vital site.

STORMCASTS' COMMAND ABILITY

To the Death: Your general calls upon his brave warriors to fight to their last breath. Pick a unit from your army that is within 12" of the Realmgate. Until your next hero phase, roll a dice each time a model from that unit is slain. On a roll of 4 or more, you can inflict 1 mortal wound on an enemy model that is within 1" of that model before it is removed from play.

CUSTODIAN'S COMMAND ABILITY

Crush the Intruders: At your general's command, horns summon nearby forces to crush the intruders without mercy. If your general uses this ability, roll a dice. If the result is 4 or more, set up a new unit anywhere within 6" of any edge of the battlefield that is more than 9" from the enemy. This counts as that unit's move in the following movement phase.

THE BATTLEFIELD

This battle takes place on a scorched plain, littered with the remnants of the fallen civilization that once called these lands home. Broken masonry and shattered buildings dot the horizon, interspersed with wild flora that has stubbornly taken root within the tortured ground. The centre of the battlefield is dominated by a towering Realmgate, the oily surface of its portal rippling with otherworldly power. The Realmgate has the Inspiring scenery rule in addition to any other rules it may have.

Inspiring: Add 1 to the Bravery of all units within 3" of this terrain feature.

You can either generate the rest of the scenery for this battle as described on the *Warhammer: Age of Sigmar* rules sheet, or use the example scenery shown on the map below.

SET-UP

Do not use the set-up instructions on the *Warhammer: Age of Sigmar* rules sheet. Instead, anything within 15" of the central Realmgate is the Stormcasts' territory, and the rest of the battlefield is the custodian's territory. The custodian sets up their army first, anywhere in their territory; the Stormcast player then sets aside all the units in their army, ready to arrive during the battle.

Custodian's Territory
Realmgate
15"
Stormcasts' Territory
Custodian's Territory

FIRST TURN

The Stormcast player always takes the first turn in the first battle round.

SUDDEN ARRIVAL

At the start of each of their hero phases, the Stormcast player must roll a dice for each unit that they put to one side during set-up. On the roll of a 3 or more, that unit is transported into the fray; set up the unit on the battlefield more than 9" from any enemy models. That is their move for the following movement phase. If a unit does not arrive, or there is no space to set up the unit using the above restrictions, the Stormcast player rolls again for that unit at the start of their next hero phase.

FORLORN HOPE

Units in the Stormcasts' force that arrive in the first battle round do not need to take battleshock tests for the duration of the entire battle.

HEROIC STAND!

If a Totem from the Stormcasts' army is within 3" of the Realmgate at the start of their hero phase it can make a heroic stand, refusing to move from that spot until the Realmgate is secured. If it does so, the Totem cannot move for the rest of the battle, but the Stormcast player can re-roll all failed hit rolls for units from their army that are within 12". In addition, when damage is inflicted upon the Totem, the Stormcast player can choose to instead inflict that damage on any unit from their army that is within 3".

VICTORY

Do not use any of the victory conditions on the *Warhammer: Age of Sigmar* rules sheet. Instead, at the end of a battle round, the Stormcast player wins a **major victory** if none of the custodian's starting models are on the battlefield, or the custodian wins a **major victory** if none of the Stormcast player's models that arrived during the first turn are on the battlefield.

If both of the above conditions are met, the result is a **draw**.

In addition, if the custodian has a third more models than their opponent, the Stormcast player can also win a **major victory** by having at least one model within 3" of the Realmgate at the end of the fourth battle round.

THE STORM ENTERS GHYRAN

Even as the first Stormcast Eternal assaults struck Aqshy, so did Sigmar hurl more bolts. Into the realm of Ghyran the God-King loosed much of his might, for he sensed the realm, and his one-time ally Alarielle, were in great peril. Thus did the Stormcast Eternals enter those embattled territories.

Once, Ghyran – also known as the Realm of Life, or the Jade Kingdoms – was a place of great growth and wonder. From barren to abundant, the entire realm flowed in cycles – both seasonal and mystic. When in bloom, no lands were more verdant or bountiful.

In the Age of Myth, Alarielle, the Queen of the Radiant Woods, and ultimate ruler of the Jade Kingdoms, joined Sigmar's pantheon. However, Alarielle grew despondent, increasingly withdrawing into her beloved realm. She abandoned her allies even before the onset of the great invasions that marked what is now called the Age of Chaos, and when her lands were besieged there was no aid to call upon.

All the Chaos powers sought to conquer, as was their nature. Yet there was one who coveted the bountiful lands of Ghyran above all else – Nurgle, the Plaguefather. The God of Blight sent forth his plague legions and Rotbringers, turning the fertile richness of Ghyran into putrescent decay.

When Sigmar's storm broke over Ghyran, and lightning strikes brought down Stormcast Eternals, they found a vast realm that was reeling. A fog of disease rolled over the land, corrupting all it touched. Elder forests had been reduced into sentient, crawling bogs, rot-hearted beasts prowled the lands, and everywhere Chaos forces conquered and destroyed. Knights-Azyros led contingents to seek out the hidden paths that might lead them to Athelwyrd, Alarielle's Hidden Vale. It was Sigmar's hope to re-establish old ties, to bond with sylvaneth forces and begin the long task of ridding Ghyran of Chaos. While the Knights-Azyros sought the illusion-hidden trails, the main Stormcast Eternal assaults targeted vital Realmgates. Elements of more than a score of Stormhosts were sent down as a flurry of lightning blazed over the verdant kingdoms.

Of all the Realmgate assaults, there was one in particular which gave Sigmar great foreboding: that of the Gates of Dawn. For that mission, the God-King sent forth the Hallowed Knights.

LORD-CELESTANT GARDUS

Honour. Sacrifice. Duty. These are important concepts to all Stormcast Eternals, but none revere their sacred task like the warriors of the Hallowed Knights. Only those who worshipped Sigmar and called upon him for aid against the horrors of Chaos found themselves selected by incandescent rapture to join that Stormhost. There, in Sigmaron, they were reforged and inducted into the devout Hallowed Knights, with the message that it was not Sigmar who would help them, but rather they that would aid Sigmar. This elevation filled Gardus, consuming him utterly. No one trained harder or performed more impressively in the Gladitorium than did Gardus, for the honour the God-King bestowed weighed heavy upon him. Indeed, despite his great successes during the training battles of the Gladitorium, Gardus remained apprehensive about his ability to live up to the divine blessings gifted to him until his first true combat as a Stormcast Eternal at the Battle for the Gates of Dawn. There, he would prove himself beyond doubt.

With the sudden shock and ferocity of their attacks, the Stormcast Eternals won many triumphs across Ghyran. Three Chambers of the Hammers of Sigmar captured the Oakgate, while elements of many Stormhosts worked together to seal off the corrupted Five Gates of Ghyran. The entire Sons of Mallus Stormhost seized the Passage of Thorns. Such was the wrath of their assault that they burnt down the corrupted Thornwood in the process.

In that initial celestial onslaught, six Realmgates were eventually taken, giving the Stormcast Eternals further inroads in their search for Alarielle. It seemed as if the Hallowed Knights would add to those triumphs, for they unleashed righteous fury, smiting the Chaos Lord that ruled the diseased Ghyrtribe. Yet even in the moment of their first victory, the Hallowed Knights realised something was amiss.

The Gates of Dawn were corrupted, for they no longer served as a pathway to distant Aqshy. Instead, the Realmgate was a tentacle-lined passage that led to the Garden of Nurgle – the loathsome birthplace of pestilence and the centre of the Plaguefather's immeasurable might. The filth of ages came out of those gates now, as the colossal greater daemon Bolathrax took the field. Aided by the rich flow of vile powers, he summoned Plaguebearers beyond count. So the battle began anew.

Under Gardus' commands, the Hallowed Knights reformed to combat the Plaguebearers that encircled them. Against such relentless numbers, there was little hope of victory, yet the Hallowed Knights fought on. If it was to be their fate to fall before that onslaught, then each warrior wanted to make his end a glorious one, worthy of the great honour of being reforged to serve Sigmar once again.

The God-King had not abandoned his most faithful of Stormhosts. Anticipating the import of this growing clash in the Ghyrtract Fen, Sigmar had held back reserve forces. From the skies raged more lightnings, sending into that battle further chambers of Hallowed Knights, as well as chambers from the Astral Templars Stormhost. The newly arrived Stormcast Eternals drove deep into their foe. However, drawing upon a mixture of life energies and purest corruption, Bolathrax was swollen with power, and summoned more minions. For every daemon that fell, three more materialised. Soon, even the zealous impetus of the Astral Templars became mired, weighed down beneath the daemons' numbers.

The stalemate was seemingly broken when the sky peeled away and out poured the skaven. They had gouged a gnaw-hole into reality and scurried forth to aid their diseased allies.

Seeing that victory could not be achieved whilst the foe drew upon unlimited reinforcements, Lord-Celestant Gardus took it upon himself to close the Gates of Dawn. Alone, he duelled the massive Great Unclean One Bolathrax, yet the foul fiend recovered from every wound. Seeing there was no other way, the Lord-Celestant leapt into the archway, hoping to destroy it from within, or draw Bolathrax away from the battle. The plan worked, but so girthly was the Greater Daemon, now, that its tremendous bulk tore apart the gateway, breaking the magical link, and trapping Gardus on the wrong side.

The battle still may have gone ill for the remaining Stormcast Eternals, but for the arrival of another army: the sylvaneth wargroves. At last the tree-spirits of the Jade Kingdoms came to aid the Stormcast Eternals. The daemons fell to their combined might, and the skaven fled, dismayed.

All across Ghyran thunderbolts continued to strike, as the Stormcast Eternals attempted to wrest the Jade Kingdoms from out of the beslimed grasp of the conquering armies of the Chaos invaders. Sigmar's Tempest clashed head-on with the roiling fug of Nurgle. Every day more Stormhosts arrived, pouring forth from out of reclaimed Realmgates. At times Sigmar's armies found aid in the form of sylvaneth forces; they appeared out of nowhere to join the fight against the daemon legions and rampaging Chaos warbands. Yet all too often the Stormcast Eternals found themselves fighting alone, unguided and unaided in the hellish rotscape that had spread across those lands.

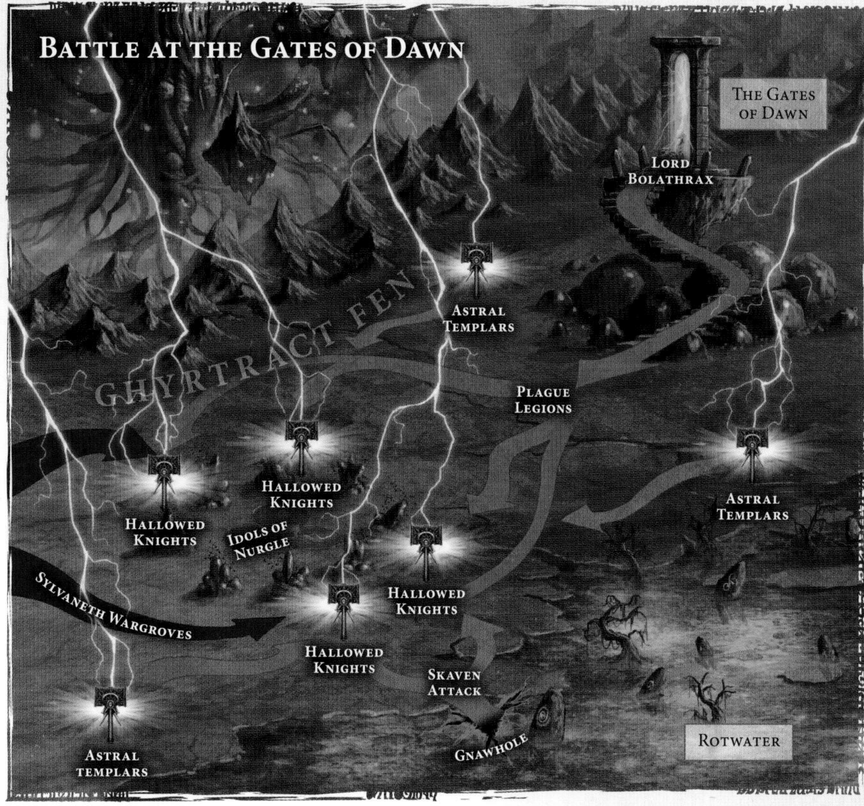

Queen Alarielle had recognised the marks of Sigmar upon the Stormcast Eternals, but ever cyclical in her moods, she was not yet in her war aspect. She turned away emissaries, preferring instead to remain in her illusion-hidden vale. Alongside foul disease, despair had sunk into the lands and the Radiant Queen's own heart. Unable to find Alarielle to beseech her to join the cause, the Stormcast Eternals seemed doomed to battle alone.

It was Gardus of the Hallowed Knights that found the solution. Returned from the Garden of Nurgle, the battered but unbroken Lord-Celestant told of many secrets learned during his harrowing escape from the Realm of Chaos, including the location of Alarielle. Gardus led several Stormhosts spearheading into Rotwater Blight. After many battles, including unblocking the Oak of Ages Past and freeing the River Vitalis of contamination, the Stormhosts at last entered Athelwyrd, the domain of Alarielle. Unbeknownst to them, however, the Stormcast Eternals had been followed. The armies of Chaos streamed into Alarielle's sanctum – daemons, brayherds, skaven, and Blightkings beyond count, bringing with them a deluge of corrupting filth.

Side by side the Stormcast Eternals battled, fighting and falling alongside the sylvaneth forces. In that struggle, the forces of Order slew many for each of their own that was struck down, yet slowly they were forced backwards. Even when Alarielle donned the mantle of war and joined the fray they could not turn the tide. Before the deluge of pestilence that rained from the skies, there could be no victory. Ultimately they were driven from Athelwyrd, forced to abandon Alarielle's sanctum. However, the Stormcast Eternals had perhaps, at last, gained an ally in the continuing battle for the Jade Kingdoms.

AGAINST THE HORDE

Despite Sigmar's trepidation, his Stormcast Eternals appeared to have launched a successful assault on the Gates of Dawn, driving the forces of Nurgle before them and claiming the Realmgate. Then came Bolathrax. Around him was a cloud of flies so large that the swarm blotted out the sunlight. At the Greater Daemon's command, the flies began to coalesce into Plaguebearers beyond number. Within moments, the battle for the Gates of Dawn became a desperate battle to strike down the Great Unclean One and sever the limitless reinforcements at his command, lest the embattled Stormhosts be overwhelmed.

Using this battleplan you can refight this battle, or recreate another clash between a beleaguered Stormcast army and an overwhelming enemy force that seeks ingress through a captured Realmgate.

THE ARMIES

One player takes command of the Stormcast army, and the other represents the mastermind leading the enemy forces through the Realmgate.

The general of each army has a unique command ability, shown below, in addition to any others they have.

STORMCASTS' OBJECTIVES

By channelling aetheric energies through the Realmgate, the enemy general is gathering a host of impossible size to claim this hard-won battlefield. You must rally your embattled Stormhost and take the fight to the foe once more. Your only chance of securing victory this day is to strike down the lynchpin of the enemy's reinforcements that are pouring into the fray. The odds are long, but the power of Sigmar surges through your veins and you know that there remains hope that you can emerge victorious.

MASTERMIND'S OBJECTIVES

After crushing your disposable vassals, the Stormcasts foolishly believe themselves victorious. They are mistaken, and you will make them pay for their arrogance. Summon forth your legions and bury your enemies beneath an overwhelming horde of warriors. While you control the Realmgate there is no limit to the power at your disposal. Seize the advantage, and watch Sigmar's chosen drown in blood.

MASTERMIND'S COMMAND ABILITY

Manifest Reinforcements: Tapping into the vast reservoir of power beyond the Realmgate, your general summons otherworldly reinforcements to the battle. Set up a new unit as part of your army so that all of its models are within 12" of the Realmgate and not within 9" of any enemy models. This counts as that unit's move in the following movement phase.

STORMCASTS' COMMAND ABILITY

No Surrender: Your general calls upon their celestial kin to fight on against seemingly impossible odds. Until your next hero phase you can roll two dice for any battleshock tests you make for units in your army, discarding the dice with the highest result.

THE BATTLEFIELD

The battle takes place in a heavily wooded environment surrounding a Realmgate. The landscape has seen heavy fighting throughout the past hours, and corpses and broken terrain lie strewn across the battlefield.

You can either generate the scenery for this battle as described on the *Warhammer: Age of Sigmar* rules sheet, adding a Baleful Realmgate within 6" of the centre of the mastermind's battlefield edge, or use the example scenery shown on the map below.

SET-UP

Do not use the set-up instructions on the *Warhammer: Age of Sigmar* rules sheet. Instead, each force's territory is marked on the map below. The players take turns to set up units, until they have set up all the units they want to use or have run out of space.

Having only just slain the last of their previous opponents moments before, the Stormcast forces are still spread out across the battlefield. The Stormcast player must therefore roll a dice before setting up each of their units and consult the map below to determine where it must be set up. Any units that cannot be set up in the area rolled for them must be set aside, and will move on to the battlefield from the southern edge in their first movement phase.

FIRST TURN

Both players roll a dice to determine who takes the first battle round, as described on the *Warhammer: Age of Sigmar* rules sheet.

24"
Mastermind's Territory
24"
24"
24"
12"
Stormcasts' Territory
1-2
3-4
5-6

UNNATURAL REGROWTH

Not only can the mastermind's general utilise the vast power beyond the Realmgate to summon a numberless horde, but they can also draw upon its energies to heal their own torn flesh. In each of the mastermind's hero phases, their general heals D3 wounds.

THE PATH OF HEROISM

The Stormcast commanders know how dangerous their enemy's general is, and understand that it is their solemn duty to deal with this terrible threat. The Stormcast player can re-roll failed hit rolls for any of their Heroes that are within 12" of the mastermind's general.

VICTORY

Do not use any of the victory conditions on the *Warhammer: Age of Sigmar* rules sheet. If a player has no models on the battlefield at the end of a battle round, the battle ends and their opponent wins a **major victory**. Otherwise, the battle ends after the fifth battle round.

If the mastermind's general is not on the battlefield when the battle ends, the Stormcast player wins. This is a **major victory** if at least half of their starting models are still on the battlefield. Otherwise, it is a **minor victory**.

If the mastermind's general is on the battlefield at the end of the battle, the mastermind wins. This is a **major victory** if at least half the Stormcasts' starting models have been slain. Otherwise, it is a **minor victory**.

HINTS & TIPS

This is a difficult battleplan for the Stormcast player. Due to the constant stream of reinforcements that the mastermind's general can bring into play, this battle can swiftly spiral out of control. As a result, they must be as aggressive as possible in the early stages of the game in order to corner the mastermind's general. Yet the Stormcast player must also find a balance between aggressive opening moves and reforming their scattered units into a more cohesive force. With such challenging victory conditions, this is a great battleplan to refight afterwards, swapping roles to see if your opponent can do any better!

THE TEST OF METAL

Sigmar's Stormhosts took war to each of the oppressed realms, including the scattered kingdoms of Chamon, the Realm of Metal. Sigmar longed to find and reunite with old allies there, and the God-King also suspected a secret for which he had long sought lay hidden in that corrupted realm.

In Chamon, as with all the realms they entered, the Stormcast Eternals sought to seize control of Realmgates. Additionally, Knights-Azyros led reconnaissance forays to seek out the god Grungni and his duardin followers.

Once Sigmar had counted Grungni, the Forge-God of the duardin, amongst the closest of all allies. As the power of Chaos grew, many rifts opened in the God-King's pantheon, some beyond hope of redemption. Grungni and his sturdy followers had always proven loyal in the past, and it was the Master Smith himself who aided Sigmar in the Reforging process that created the first Stormcast Eternal, but the Forge-God had been absent now for many years.

Meanwhile, the Celestial Vindicators searched the Valleys of Anvrok for the hidden Realmgate. While they did so, other eyes espied them. The sorcerer, Ephryx, the Ninth Disciple of the Ninth Tower of Tzeentch, watched the lightning strikes that bore these newcomers. He saw the gleam of immortality and he instantly knew his foe.

Long ago, Sigmar had lost his weapon, the matchless warhammer, Ghal Maraz. Tricked by Tzeentch's master illusion, the God-King had hurled the weapon not into a foe, but into a rift in reality. Like a hurtling comet, it passed through many realms, drawn at last by the heavy pull of the Realm of Metal.

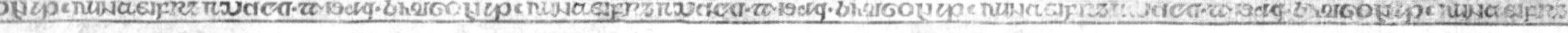

LORD-CELESTANT THOSTOS BLADESTORM

Like all the Celestial Vindicators, vengeance was ever foremost upon Thostos' mind. The firstborn son of the guild-king Glothian, Thostos returned from a slayerquest to find his people butchered in his absence. His guilt-haunted rampage was halted only when Sigmar granted his wish for an eternity in which to enact revenge. Such was the fury of the young prince's desire that the God-King's knew immediately which stormhost to place him in. As a Lord-Celestant of the Celestial Vindicators, it was Thostos who led the initial attack against the Eldritch Fortress of Anvrok. Thostos' assault wreaked havoc upon the walls built to trammel Ghal Maraz, undoing the works of the sorcerer Ephryx. During the battle, the Lord-Celestant was turned to living sigmarite by wild transformative power, but still he fought on. Only a spell of surpassing power halted his wild attack. Reforged in Sigmar's vaults, Thostos' body is flesh once more, but echoes of his strange death persist. Though immortal, each Stormcast stands to lose much with each Reforging.

It was Tzeentch's master plan to break apart Sigmar's pantheon, and to strip the God-King of his greatest weapon. The God of Sorcery desired the hammer for his own, to siphon its storm of energy for his own diabolic plans. By scrying magics unequalled, Tzeentch tracked the hammer to its landing site, but such was the power of the artefact it proved anathema to Chaos, so that even Tzeentch's mightiest greater daemons could not move it, nor bear to gaze long upon it.

This conundrum did not long delay Tzeentch, however; he soon manipulated his minions to cast down the monument men had raised over the fallen object, and covens of Lords of Change wove powerful spells of concealment to enshroud the mystic aura given off by Ghal Maraz. Years went by, and Chaos grew stronger. The city of men that had risen around the hammer was destroyed, and, layer by layer, a great stronghold was built in its stead – the Eldritch Fortress. Deep inside its central keep, thick chains of magic tethered the warhammer, keeping it from returning to the hand of its divine master.

For the many centuries that followed, the precious artefact was guarded by the sorcerer Ephryx, a pawn in Tzeentch's uncountable schemes. Tzeentch himself had long meant to devote time to destroy that hateful warhammer, yet always the Master of Intrigue was delayed, sidetracked by other strands of fate that called more urgently. In the meantime, Ephryx knew the power source must be secreted and guarded at all cost.

Ephryx was steeped in arcane wisdom, yet foolish pride and his own scheming nature became his undoing. It was he who lured the Stormcast Eternals to the fortress. Ephryx wished to slay these powerful newcomers, and to use their own energies to further his own mad schemes. So were the Celestial Vindicators lured into besieging the Eldritch Fortress, although they knew not that it guarded Sigmar's most sought-after treasure.

The Eldritch Fortress was protected by deadly enchantments and warrior hordes, yet the Celestial Vindicators were resolute. Steeled by sigmarite and thoughts of vengeance, they advanced, smashing down the gates in the fury of their assault. Across courtyard and battlement, the opposing sides charged and counter-attacked, while storm bolts from Azyr blazed down.

Aware that his plan was backfiring and his foes were too powerful to contain, Ephryx unleashed the overburdened energies of the Eldritch Fortress. The explosion that followed destroyed the Celestial Vindicators as they surged towards victory, but even as they died, several saw the glorious light issuing from the heart of the fortress. Back to Sigmaron were the spirits of the slain Stormcast Eternals returned, and when they were reforged once more Sigmar asked them what they had seen – for his suspicions of that spell-shielded fortress had been growing. When he realised that his lost weapon had been located, a great assault was prepared.

When next the lightning struck in Anvrok, the Stormcast Eternals arrived in force. At the fore were the Hammers of Sigmar and the Celestial Vindicators. They found ambushes awaiting them, but to their horror, the Eldritch Fortress had disappeared.

By translocating the Eldritch Fortress from the Shattered City to the Great Crucible – a floating disc that hovered high in the skies – Ephryx had sought to keep it from the reach of Sigmar's fresh-forged armies. Ultimately he intended to use its power for a greater change; a coven of Lords of Change began a ritual which, if seen to completion, would bring all of Chamon into Tzeentch's labyrinthine domain.

With the aid of the spirits of Anvrok's dead and the stars themselves, the Stormcast Eternals found their quarry and besieged the Eldritch Fortress once again. Armies and spellfire opposed them, yet onwards they pressed, an indomitable force that would not be stopped. Despite suffering horrific losses, the Stormcast at last pressed home their assault, storming into the circle of daemons and disrupting their ritual. Ghal Maraz was secured and the Eldritch Fortress tumbled into the void, foiling one of Tzeentch's many plots.

The Great Crucible

Citadel of Thrond

Sigmar's Tempest

Denvrok Precipice

The Void

Argent Falls

The Alchemist's Moon

The Flames of Argentine

The Silverway

Bright Tor Mountains

Defence of the Silverway

Vaulten Range

The Siege of the Eldritch Fortress

Silver River

Anvrok

Elixia, The Shattered City

Argentine
The Silver Wyrm

Denvrok

Vytrix
The Crystal Cockatrice

Mercuria Vale

Kantrok

BATTLEPLAN
RETRIEVE THE RELIC

Ghal Maraz, the irreplaceable hammer of the God-King Sigmar, has been found. The Stormcast Eternals are gathered in force and dutifully march to reclaim their master's ultimate weapon, yet their task will prove to be far from easy. A mighty fortress has been raised about the relic, and a powerful host sworn to the Dark Gods stands ready to defend its walls. Only through implacable courage and determination can the Stormhosts hope to emerge triumphant and return to Sigmaron with their prize.

Though there is only one Ghal Maraz, there are many treasures that would aid Sigmar's forces if they were claimed, many of which lie in strongholds and armoured vaults under the watchful eye of the enemy. With this battleplan you can enact the final march to reclaim Sigmar's hammer, or the liberation of any number of lesser relics.

THE ARMIES

One player takes command of the Stormcast army, and the other represents the defenders of the coveted relic.

The general of each army has a unique command ability, shown below, in addition to any others they have.

STORMCASTS' OBJECTIVES

The location of a great and terrible relic has been discovered – an artefact so powerful that Sigmar has charged you with the task of retrieving it, no matter the cost. Your objective is straightforward, if not simple to achieve – sack the enemy fortress and butcher its defenders in order to claim the relic in the name of your lord.

DEFENDER'S OBJECTIVES

The followers of Sigmar have heard rumour of the fabled relic that lies ensconced within your keep's vault and now lay siege to your stronghold with a mighty war host. As the steward of this priceless artefact, it is your duty to see the enemy broken before your walls and slaughtered in their entirety. If the Stormcast army is too great in size to repel, it will be enough to endure their attacks long enough for the relic to be spirited away to safety.

STORMCASTS' COMMAND ABILITY

Assail the Walls: Your general orders the storming of the walls. Your general and all units from your army that are within 12" of them when this ability is used cannot be harmed by the Walls of Death scenery rule until your next hero phase.

DEFENDER'S COMMAND ABILITY

Hold the Battlements: Calling upon his warriors to fight or die in defence of the walls, your general inspires his men to fight on until their last breath. Your general and all units from your army that are within 12" of them when they use this ability can re-roll save rolls of a 1 until your next hero phase if they are within or on a Malefic Gate, Skull Keep, Overlord Bastion or Fortress Wall.

THE BATTLEFIELD

The western half of the battlefield is dominated by the fortress that houses the fabled relic.

You can use the example scenery shown on the map below, or the defender can set up scenery to their liking to represent the fortress created by their archimancers. If so, the defender must set up at least one Malefic Gate and two Skull Keeps or Overlord Bastions.

SET-UP

The players take it in turns to set up units, as described on the *Warhammer: Age of Sigmar* rules sheet. The defender can set up their units anywhere within 24" of the western edge of the battlefield, and must set up at least half of their units on or within the walls of the fortress. The Stormcast player can set up their units anywhere that is more than 36" away from the western edge of the battlefield.

OPENING VOLLEY

After set-up has been completed, any units in the defender's army that were set up on a Malefic Gate, Skull Keep, Overlord Bastion or Fortress Wall can loose an opening volley, attacking with any missile weapons they are carrying. After these attacks have been resolved, any of the Stormcast player's units that suffered casualties must take an immediate battleshock test.

FIRST TURN

The Stormcast player always takes the first turn in the first battle round.

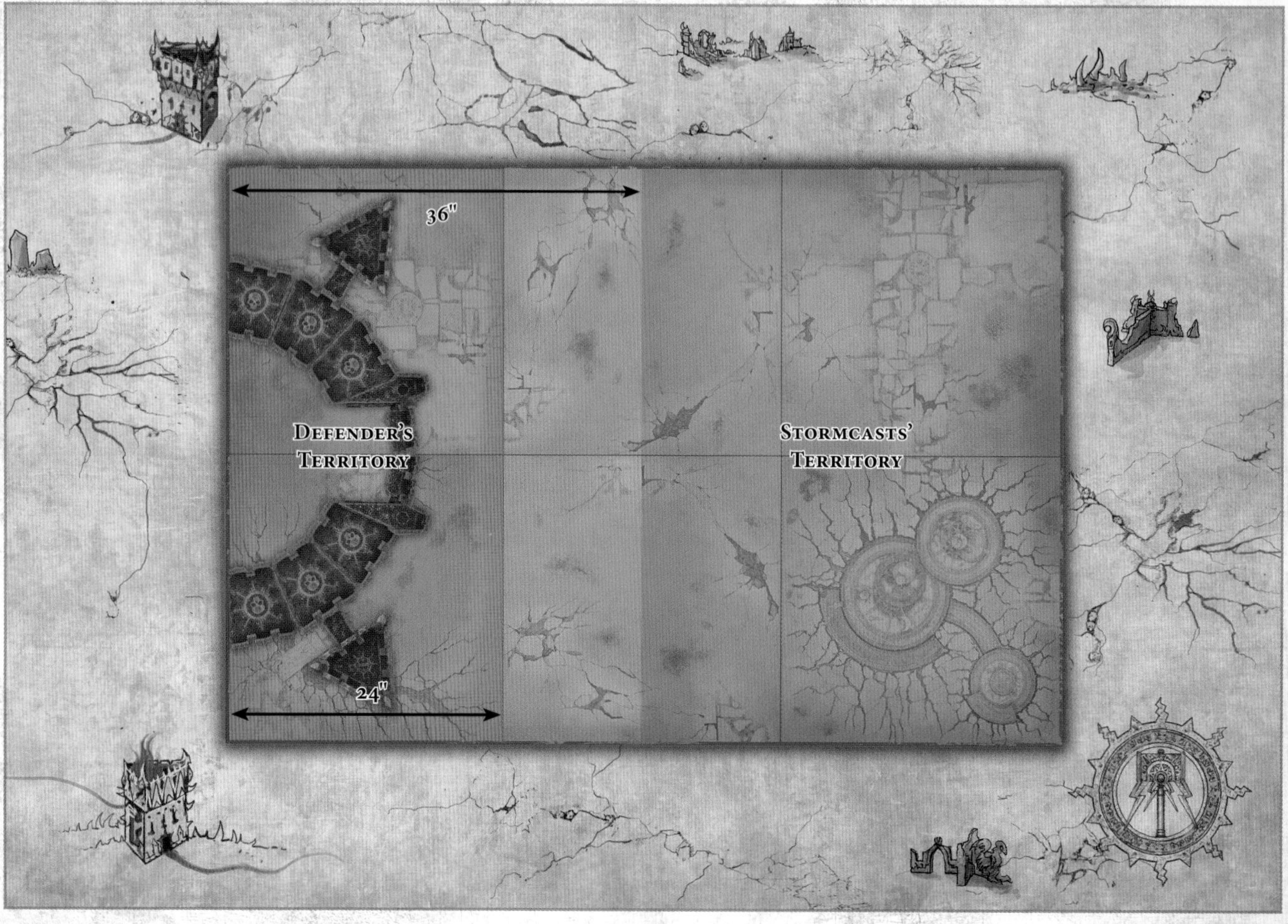

36"
Defender's Territory
Stormcasts' Territory
24"

MOLTEN RAIN

If both players roll the same number when determining who will take the first turn in a battle round, the roiling clouds above begin to spit molten rain. Both players must immediately make a single save roll for each of their units on the battlefield. If the save roll is passed, that unit's armour has protected them from the worst effects of the molten rain; if the save roll is failed, that unit suffers D3 mortal wounds. Once this has been resolved, the players roll again to see who will take the first turn. Molten rain can only fall once per battle round, even if this second roll is also a tie.

FORCED MARCH

Galvanised into action by the opening volley of the castle's defenders, the leaders of the Stormcasts bellow out orders to those under their command, urging them to hasten their attack on the wall. Units in the Stormcast army that are within 6" of a friendly HERO can make a forced march. Units that make a forced march roll 2 dice and add the highest result to their Move characteristic when they run.

VICTORY

Do not use any of the victory conditions on the *Warhammer: Age of Sigmar* rules sheet. Instead, if none of a player's starting models are on the battlefield at the end of a battle round, the game ends and their opponent wins a **major victory**.

If the Stormcast player has a third more models than their opponent, the defender can also win a **major victory** by having at least one of their starting models on the battlefield at the end of the sixth battle round.

Otherwise, the battle lasts for six battle rounds. At the end of the battle, the defender wins a **minor victory** if they have more models on or within the fortress walls than the Stormcast player; otherwise, the Stormcast player wins a **minor victory**.

SIGMAR'S WRATH

WARSCROLLS

The warriors and creatures that battle in the Mortal Realms are incredibly diverse, each one fighting with their own unique weapons and combat abilities. To represent this, every model has a warscroll that lists the characteristics, weapons and abilities that apply to the model.

Every Citadel Miniature in the Warhammer range has its own warscroll, which provides you with all of the information needed to use that model in a game of *Warhammer: Age of Sigmar*. This means that you can use any Citadel Miniatures in your collection as part of an army as long as you have the right warscrolls.

When fighting a battle, simply refer to the warscrolls for the models you are using. Warscrolls for all of the other models in the *Warhammer: Age of Sigmar* range are available from Games Workshop. Just visit our website at games-workshop.com for more information on how to obtain them.

The key below explains what you will find on a warscroll, and the *Warhammer: Age of Sigmar* rules sheet explains how this information is used in a game. The warscroll also includes a picture of a unit of the models that the warscroll describes, and a short piece of text explaining the background for the models and how they fight.

WARSCROLL

1 LORD-CELESTANT

Inspiring leaders of the Warrior Chambers, the Lord-Celestants march to war mantled in the might of the storm. None can escape the vengeful blows of their runeblades and sigmarite hammers – should any try, the Lord-Celestant swirls his armoured cloak, loosing a hurtling cloud of sorcerous hammers that strike down the cowardly foe.

2

MOVE 5"
WOUNDS 5
SAVE 3+
BRAVERY 9

MELEE WEAPONS	Range	Attacks	To Hit	To Wound	Rend	Damage
Sigmarite Runeblade	1"	4	3+	3+	-1	1
Warhammer	1"	2	4+	3+	-	1

3 **DESCRIPTION**
A Lord-Celestant is a single model. He is armed with a fearsome Sigmarite Runeblade and a Warhammer, and wears a Sigmarite Warcloak.

4 **ABILITIES**
Inescapable Vengeance: If this model has made a charge move this turn, it can make 1 extra attack with each of its melee weapons.

Sigmarite Warcloak: In your shooting phase, you can unleash D6 hammers from this model's Sigmarite Warcloak. Pick an enemy unit within 16" of this model for each hammer that is unleashed, then roll a dice for each unit you picked. On a roll of 4 or more the unit suffers a mortal wound. Note that you can pick the same unit more than once in a phase.

COMMAND ABILITY
Furious Retribution: If this model is your general and uses this ability, then until your next hero phase you can add 1 to the result of any hit rolls in the combat phase for this model and friendly STORMCAST ETERNAL units within 9" of him.

KEYWORDS ORDER, CELESTIAL, HUMAN, STORMCAST ETERNAL, HERO, LORD-CELESTANT 5

117

1. **Title:** The name of the model that the warscroll describes.

2. **Characteristics:** This set of characteristics tells you how fast, powerful and brave the model is, and how effective its weapons are.

3. **Description:** The description tells you what weapons the model can be armed with, and what upgrades (if any) it can be given. The description will also tell you if the model is fielded on its own as a single model, or as part of a unit. If the model is fielded as part of a unit, then the description will say how many models the unit should have (if you don't have enough models to field a unit, you can still field one unit with as many models as you have available).

4. **Abilities:** Abilities are things that the model can do during a game that are not covered by the standard game rules.

5. **Keywords:** All models have a list of keywords. Sometimes a rule will say that it only applies to models that have a specific keyword.

HINTS & TIPS

The following hints and tips will help you get the most from your warscrolls:

Modifiers: Many warscrolls include modifiers that can affect characteristics. For example, a rule might add 1 to the Move characteristic of a model, or subtract 1 from the result of a hit roll. Modifiers are cumulative.

Random Values: Sometimes, the Move or weapon characteristics on a warscroll will have random values. For example, the Move characteristic for a model might be 2D6 (two dice rolls added together), whereas the Attacks characteristic of a weapon might be D6.

When a unit with a random Move characteristic is selected to move in the movement phase, roll the indicated number of dice. The total of the dice rolled is the Move characteristic for all models in the unit for the duration of that movement phase.

Generate any random values for a weapon (except Damage) each time it is chosen as the weapon for an attack. Roll once and apply the result to all such weapons being used in the attack. The result applies for the rest of that phase. For Damage, generate a value for each weapon that inflicts damage.

When to Use Abilities: Abilities that are used at the start of a phase must be carried out before any other actions. For example, abilities carried out at the start of the movement phase must be used before any models are moved. By the same token, abilities used at the end of the phase are carried out after all normal activities for the phase are complete.

If you can use several abilities at the same time, you can decide in which order they are used. If both players can carry out abilities at the same time, the player whose turn is taking place uses their abilities first.

Save of '-': Some models have a Save of '-'. This means that they automatically fail all save rolls (do not make the roll, even if modifiers apply).

Keywords: Keywords are sometimes linked to (or tagged) by a rule. For example, a rule might say that it applies to 'all STORMCAST ETERNALS'. This means that it would apply to models that have the Stormcast Eternal keyword on their warscroll.

Keywords can also be a useful way to decide which models to include in an army. For example, if you want to field a Stormcast Eternals army, just use models that have the Stormcast Eternal keyword.

Minimum Range: Some weapons have a minimum range. For example 6"-48". The weapon cannot shoot at an enemy unit that is within the minimum range.

LORD-CELESTANT ON DRACOTH

The Lord-Celestants that lead each Stormhost are exceptional warriors even amongst their immortal kind. Majestic upon their lightning-spitting Dracoths, Lord-Celestants bolster their brethren's resolve as they plunge into the thick of the fray. With the power to ride the storm in flashes of azure light, their vengeance is both violent and inescapable.

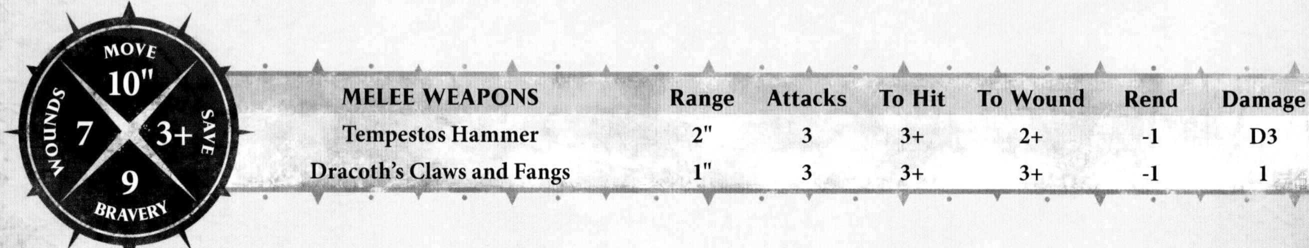

MELEE WEAPONS	Range	Attacks	To Hit	To Wound	Rend	Damage
Tempestos Hammer	2"	3	3+	2+	-1	D3
Dracoth's Claws and Fangs	1"	3	3+	3+	-1	1

DESCRIPTION

A Lord-Celestant on Dracoth is a single model. He is armed with a Tempestos Hammer and rides a Dracoth. The Dracoth fights with its ferocious Claws and Fangs.

ABILITIES

Inescapable Vengeance: If this model has made a charge move this turn, it can make D3 extra attacks with its Tempestos Hammer.

Intolerable Damage: If the wound roll for the Dracoth's Claws and Fangs attack is 6 or more, then that attack has a Damage characteristic of D6 rather than 1.

Storm Breath: You can make a storm breath attack with this model in your shooting phase. To do so, pick a point on the battlefield that is within 12" of this model. Roll a dice for each unit (friend or foe) that is within 2" of the point that you picked. On a roll of 4 or more, the unit being rolled for suffers D3 mortal wounds.

COMMAND ABILITY

Lord of the Host: If this model is your general and uses this ability, until your next hero phase you do not have to take battleshock tests for this model or any friendly unit with the Stormcast Eternal keyword that is within 24" of this model at the start of the battleshock phase.

KEYWORDS	ORDER, CELESTIAL, HUMAN, STORMCAST ETERNAL, HERO, LORD-CELESTANT

LORD-CELESTANT

Inspiring leaders of the Warrior Chambers, the Lord-Celestants march to war mantled in the might of the storm. None can escape the vengeful blows of their runeblades and sigmarite hammers – should any try, the Lord-Celestant swirls his armoured cloak, loosing a hurtling cloud of sorcerous hammers that strike down the cowardly foe.

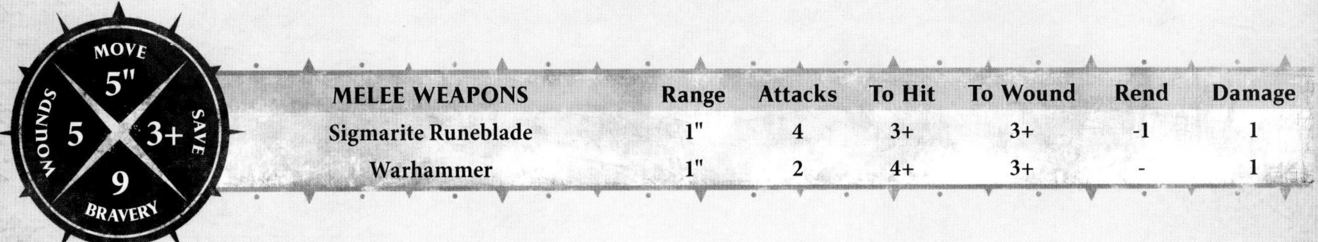

MELEE WEAPONS	Range	Attacks	To Hit	To Wound	Rend	Damage
Sigmarite Runeblade	1"	4	3+	3+	-1	1
Warhammer	1"	2	4+	3+	-	1

DESCRIPTION

A Lord-Celestant is a single model. He is armed with a fearsome Sigmarite Runeblade and a Warhammer, and wears a Sigmarite Warcloak.

ABILITIES

Inescapable Vengeance: If this model has made a charge move this turn, it can make 1 extra attack with each of its melee weapons.

Sigmarite Warcloak: In your shooting phase, you can unleash D6 hammers from this model's Sigmarite Warcloak. Pick an enemy unit within 16" of this model for each hammer that is unleashed, then roll a dice for each unit you picked. On a roll of 4 or more the unit suffers a mortal wound. Note that you can pick the same unit more than once in a phase.

COMMAND ABILITY

Furious Retribution: If this model is your general and uses this ability, then until your next hero phase you can add 1 to the result of any hit rolls in the combat phase for this model and friendly STORMCAST ETERNAL units within 9" of him.

KEYWORDS	ORDER, CELESTIAL, HUMAN, STORMCAST ETERNAL, HERO, LORD-CELESTANT

LORD-RELICTOR

Lord-Relictors are noble but sinister figures. Their ritual weapons and armour are replete with icons of death, for these fell guardians keep the warrior souls of the Stormcast Eternals from the gloom of the underworld. Potent healers as well as mighty warriors, their arcane powers channel the glory of Sigmar and call storms from the darkening skies.

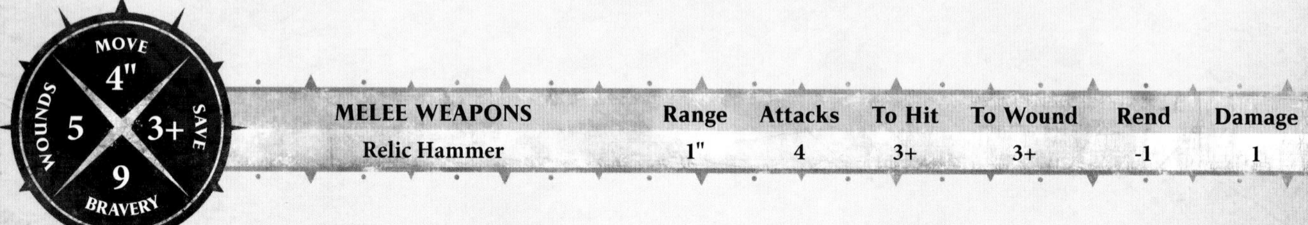

MELEE WEAPONS	Range	Attacks	To Hit	To Wound	Rend	Damage
Relic Hammer	1"	4	3+	3+	-1	1

DESCRIPTION

A Lord-Relictor is a single model. He is armed with a Relic Hammer.

ABILITIES

Lightning Storm: In your hero phase, you can declare that the Lord-Relictor will pray for a lightning storm. If you do so, pick an enemy unit that is within 12" of this model and roll a dice. On a roll of 3 or more, the unit you picked suffers D3 mortal wounds, and your opponent must subtract 1 from all hit rolls for the unit until your next hero phase. A Lord-Relictor cannot pray for a lightning storm and a healing storm in the same turn.

Healing Storm: In your hero phase, you can declare that this model is praying for a healing storm. If you do so, pick a friendly model with the STORMCAST ETERNAL keyword that is within 12" of this model and roll a dice. On a roll of 3 or more you can heal up to D3 wounds that have been suffered by the model that you picked. A Lord-Relictor cannot pray for a healing storm and a lightning storm in the same turn.

KEYWORDS ORDER, CELESTIAL, HUMAN, STORMCAST ETERNAL, HERO, PRIEST, LORD-RELICTOR

LORD-CASTELLANT

Masters of defensive warfare, the Lord-Castellants watch over their Stormcast brothers. From their warding lanterns, a glorious golden glow spills forth. This magical light has many uses, from driving back the tainted foe with its purifying aura, to shielding and healing wounded Stormcast Eternals with celestial energy.

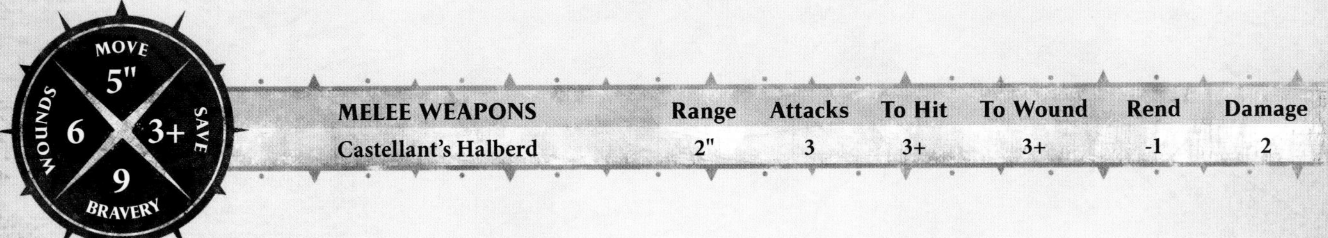

MELEE WEAPONS	Range	Attacks	To Hit	To Wound	Rend	Damage
Castellant's Halberd	2"	3	3+	3+	-1	2

DESCRIPTION

A Lord-Castellant is a single model. He is armed with a Castellant's Halberd and carries a Warding Lantern.

ABILITIES

Warding Lantern: In your hero phase the Lord-Castellant may unleash the magical energies of his Warding Lantern. If he does so, pick either a **Chaos** unit or a **Stormcast Eternal** unit that is within 12" of the Lord-Castellant.

If a **Chaos** unit is chosen it is struck by the searing light of the Celestial Realm and suffers a mortal wound. **Chaos Daemon** units cannot abide the touch of this light and suffer D3 mortal wounds instead.

If a **Stormcast Eternal** unit is chosen it is bathed in the healing energies of the lantern and you can add 1 to all save rolls it has to make until your next hero phase. In addition, until your next hero phase, each time you make a save roll of 7 or more for that unit, one model in the unit heals a wound.

KEYWORDS	ORDER, CELESTIAL, HUMAN, STORMCAST ETERNAL, HERO, LORD-CASTELLANT

KNIGHT-HERALDOR

Onwards to Glory! Forward For Sigmar! With blasts sounded upon his battle-horn, a Knight-Heraldor inspires nearby Stormcast Eternals, its eldritch energies driving them to still greater feats. So powerful are the thunderous calls of the battle-horn that the celestial shockwaves can topple buildings, fell trees or cast down the dark idols of the Chaos Gods.

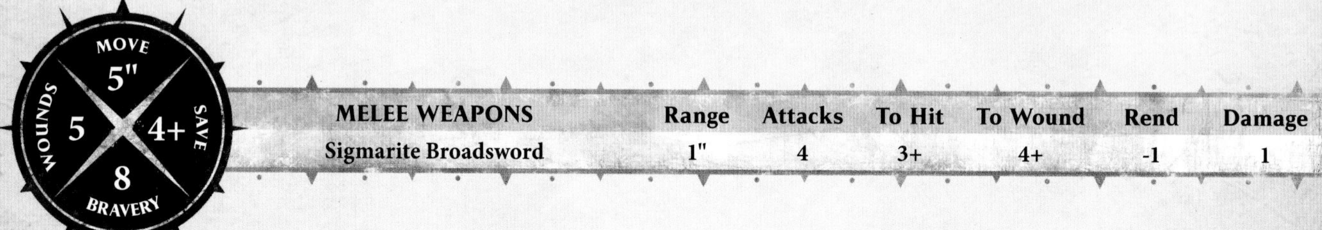

MELEE WEAPONS	Range	Attacks	To Hit	To Wound	Rend	Damage
Sigmarite Broadsword	1"	4	3+	4+	-1	1

DESCRIPTION

A Knight-Heraldor is a single model. He is armed with a Sigmarite Broadsword, and carries a Battle-horn.

ABILITIES

Onwards to Glory: In your hero phase, you can signal a call to arms with this model's Battle-horn. To do so, pick a STORMCAST ETERNAL unit that is within 10". That unit can charge this turn even if it retreats or runs in the movement phase.

Thunderblast: In your shooting phase a Knight-Heraldor can sound a thunderblast with his Battle-horn, shaking buildings to their foundations and causing trees to topple. If he does so, pick a terrain feature within 15" and roll a dice. Each unit within that many inches of the terrain feature suffers D3 mortal wounds.

KEYWORDS ORDER, CELESTIAL, HUMAN, STORMCAST ETERNAL, HERO, KNIGHT-HERALDOR

KNIGHT-VEXILLOR

Blazing with celestial energies, the banners of the Stormcast Eternals are carried proudly into battle by Knights-Vexillor, champions who can always be found in the thick of combat. These standards are more than just proud regalia; they have the power to pull down comets to smite the Stormcasts' foes, or to summon forth the swirling power of a hurricane itself.

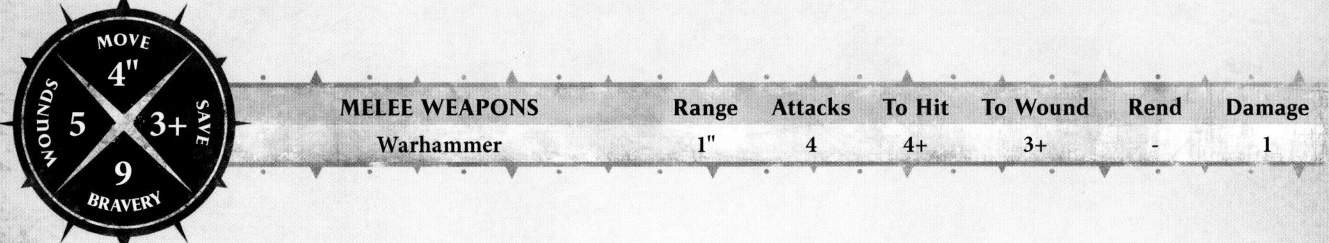

MELEE WEAPONS	Range	Attacks	To Hit	To Wound	Rend	Damage
Warhammer	1"	4	4+	3+	-	1

DESCRIPTION

A Knight-Vexillor is a single model armed with a Warhammer. Some Knights-Vexillor carry a Meteoric Standard, while others carry a Pennant of the Stormbringer.

ABILITIES

Icon of War: You can re-roll charge rolls for STORMCAST ETERNAL units in your army that are within 12", as they are inspired to glorious acts of valour.

Meteoric Standard: Once per battle, a Knight-Vexillor carrying a Meteoric Standard can call down a comet in your hero phase. To do so, pick a point on the battlefield within 24" of this model and roll two dice, adding the results together. Each unit that is within that many inches of the point that you picked suffers D3 mortal wounds.

Pennant of the Stormbringer: Once per battle, a Knight-Vexillor carrying a Pennant of the Stormbringer can summon a mighty hurricane in your hero phase. To do so, pick a STORMCAST ETERNAL unit in your army and remove it from play, then set it up anywhere more than 3" from the enemy. It cannot move in the following movement phase. After setting up the unit, roll a dice for each enemy unit within 6"; on a result of 4+, it is blasted by the gale and suffers D3 mortal wounds.

KEYWORDS	ORDER, CELESTIAL, HUMAN, STORMCAST ETERNAL, HERO, TOTEM, KNIGHT-VEXILLOR

KNIGHT-AZYROS

At the speartip of Sigmar's Tempest come the Knights-Azyros, heralds of the sky. Each bears a celestial beacon, and where a Knight-Azyros shines its light, there too can almighty Sigmar see, casting forth more Stormcast Eternals into battle. That illuminating beam is a boon to allies, and a bane to foes, most especially to the minions of Chaos.

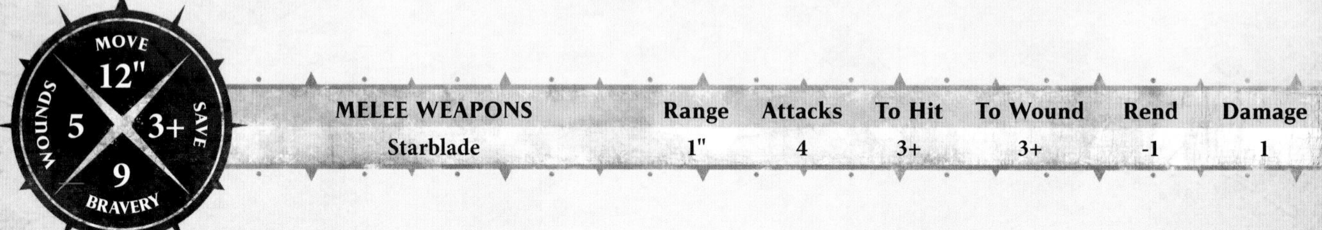

MELEE WEAPONS	Range	Attacks	To Hit	To Wound	Rend	Damage
Starblade	1"	4	3+	3+	-1	1

DESCRIPTION

A Knight-Azyros is a single model. He is armed with a Starblade and carries a Celestial Beacon.

FLY

A Knight-Azyros can fly.

ABILITIES

Leader of the Way: Stormcast Eternal units in your army that use the Lightning Strike ability to be transported to the battlefield can be set up within 5" of a Knight-Azyros, even if this would mean that they are within 9" of the enemy.

Illuminator of the Lost: In the shooting phase, you can re-roll hit rolls of 1 for attacks made against enemy units that are within 10" of a Knight-Azyros.

The Light of Sigmar: Once per battle, in your hero phase, you can declare that this model will unleash the searing light of its Celestial Beacon. If you do so, it cannot move, charge or pile in during your turn. However, each enemy unit within 8" of the Knight-Azyros when the searing light is unleashed suffers D3 mortal wounds as they are blinded and driven from the battlefield. The light is anathema to **Chaos** units, so they suffer D6 mortal wounds instead.

KEYWORDS ORDER, CELESTIAL, HUMAN, STORMCAST ETERNAL, HERO, KNIGHT-AZYROS

KNIGHT-VENATOR

The Knight-Venator is the sky-hunter, a winged archer that rains down death from above. Able to soar into position and loose volleys of precise shots, Knights-Venator hunt down and eliminate vital targets. Not even large monsters or powerful enemy leaders are safe from the deadly missile fire loosed by this soaring angel of Azyr.

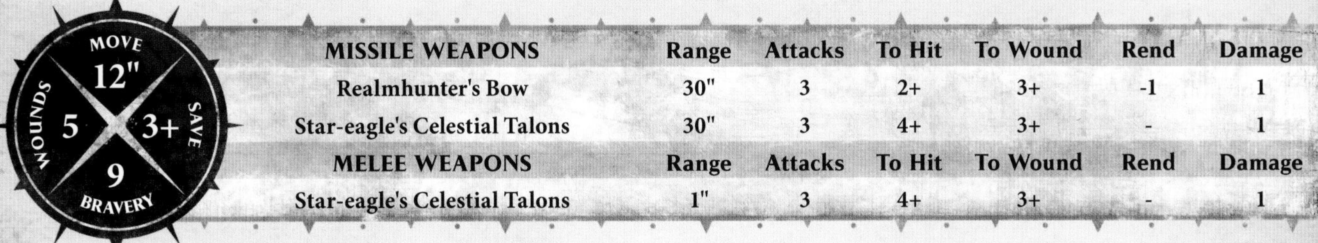

MISSILE WEAPONS	Range	Attacks	To Hit	To Wound	Rend	Damage
Realmhunter's Bow	30"	3	2+	3+	-1	1
Star-eagle's Celestial Talons	30"	3	4+	3+	-	1
MELEE WEAPONS	**Range**	**Attacks**	**To Hit**	**To Wound**	**Rend**	**Damage**
Star-eagle's Celestial Talons	1"	3	4+	3+	-	1

DESCRIPTION

A Knight-Venator is a single model. He is armed with a Realmhunter's Bow and is accompanied by a vicious Star-eagle that attacks with its Celestial Talons.

FLY

A Knight-Venator can fly.

ABILITIES

Celestial Talons: If the wound roll for the Star-eagle's Celestial Talons is 6 or more, that attack has a Rend of -3.

Star-fated Arrow: Once per battle, in your shooting phase, you can declare that this model will loose a Star-fated Arrow. When you do so, he makes 1 attack with his Realmhunter's Bow rather than 3, but it causes D3+3 Damage. If the target is a **Hero** or **Monster**, the Damage is D6+3 instead.

KEYWORDS ORDER, CELESTIAL, HUMAN, STORMCAST ETERNAL, HERO, KNIGHT-VENATOR

GRYPH-HOUNDS

Gryph-hounds are pack-hunting creatures from the realm of Azyr, noble beasts that detest corruption. Their sharp senses pierce deception as easily as their beaks and claws shred the flesh of the unfaithful. Packs of Gryph-hounds are known to ally themselves to those fighting for a just cause, and they offer loyal protection to their companions.

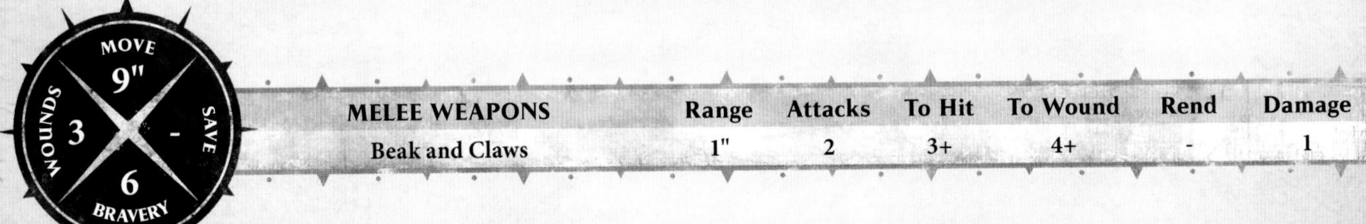

MELEE WEAPONS	Range	Attacks	To Hit	To Wound	Rend	Damage
Beak and Claws	1"	2	3+	4+	-	1

DESCRIPTION

A unit of Gryph-hounds can have any number of models. They savage their foe with their razor-sharp Beaks and Claws.

ABILITIES

Loyal Companion: Once a Gryph-hound has bonded with a companion, it will defend it to the death. A Gryph-hound makes 4 attacks with its Beak and Claws rather than 2 if the target unit is within 3" of a **Lord-Castellant**.

Darting Attacks: Gryph-hounds attack in a series of darting strikes. Immediately after this unit attacks in the combat phase, roll a dice and move each model in the unit up to that many inches.

Warning Cry: It is said that it is impossible to sneak up on a Gryph-hound. If an enemy unit is set up within 10" of this unit, roll two dice. Any unit within that many inches of the Gryph-hounds is alerted to the enemy unit's presence, and can attack it with one of its weapons as though it were your shooting phase.

KEYWORDS	ORDER, CELESTIAL, STORMCAST ETERNAL, GRYPH-HOUNDS

JUDICATORS

Whistling volleys of arrows and bolts herald the attack of the Judicators. Evil men are found wanting in their sight, and fall pierced by crackling arrows of pure lightning, or feathered with dozens of sigmarite crossbow bolts. Rank upon rank of the enemy tumble to the floor as the Judicators ply their deadly trade, until nothing remains of their foe but corpses.

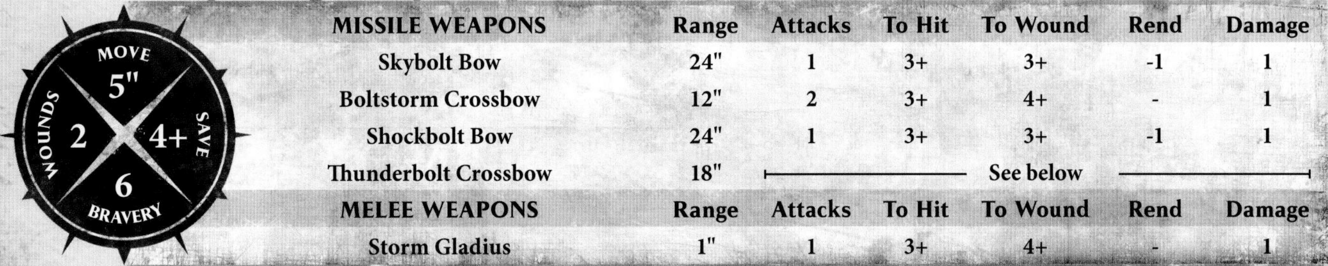

MISSILE WEAPONS	Range	Attacks	To Hit	To Wound	Rend	Damage
Skybolt Bow	24"	1	3+	3+	-1	1
Boltstorm Crossbow	12"	2	3+	4+	-	1
Shockbolt Bow	24"	1	3+	3+	-1	1
Thunderbolt Crossbow	18"			See below		
MELEE WEAPONS	**Range**	**Attacks**	**To Hit**	**To Wound**	**Rend**	**Damage**
Storm Gladius	1"	1	3+	4+	-	1

DESCRIPTION

A unit of Judicators has 5 or more models. Units of Judicators are armed with either long-ranged Skybolt Bows or rapid-firing Boltstorm Crossbows. 1 in every 5 models may instead be armed with either a Shockbolt Bow or a Thunderbolt Crossbow. In addition, every model in the unit carries a sharp Storm Gladius.

JUDICATOR-PRIME

A Judicator-Prime leads this unit. Add 1 to the hit rolls for a Judicator-Prime.

ABILITIES

Rapid Fire: If a unit of Judicators does not move in the movement phase, then you can add 1 to the Attacks characteristic of any Boltstorm Crossbows the unit uses in the shooting phase of the same turn.

Chained Lightning: If a Judicator attacking with a Shockbolt Bow scores a hit then the bolt explodes into a storm of lightning. Instead of making a single wound roll, roll a dice and make a number of wound rolls equal to the number scored.

Eternal Judgement: You may re-roll any hit rolls of 1 when a Judicator attacks a CHAOS unit in the shooting phase.

Thunderbolt Crossbow: When a model attacks with a Thunderbolt Crossbow the target is struck by a mighty blast of Celestial energy; pick an enemy unit within 18" and roll a dice. Subtract 1 from the roll if the target is a MONSTER. If the result is equal to or less than the number of models in the unit, the unit suffers D3 mortal wounds.

KEYWORDS	ORDER, CELESTIAL, HUMAN, STORMCAST ETERNAL, JUSTICAR, JUDICATORS

LIBERATORS

The hosts of the Stormcast Eternals thunder down from the Celestial Realm, intent on laying low the tyrant and the fiend. The core of each Stormhost is comprised of Liberators, men who have been magically reforged with the power of a god. In battle, these warriors use weapons of magical sigmarite to smite all enemies of Order.

MOVE 5"
WOUNDS 2
SAVE 4+
BRAVERY 6

MELEE WEAPONS	Range	Attacks	To Hit	To Wound	Rend	Damage
Warhammer	1"	2	4+	3+	-	1
Warblade	1"	2	3+	4+	-	1
Grandhammer	1"	2	4+	3+	-1	2
Grandblade	1"	2	3+	4+	-1	2

DESCRIPTION

A unit of Liberators has 5 or more models. Some units of Liberators are armed with a Warhammer in each hand, while others wield paired Warblades. Other units enter battle armed with a single Warhammer and carry Sigmarite Shields, and others still pair a Sigmarite Shield with a Warblade. In any case, 1 in every 5 models may instead be armed with either a Grandhammer, or a Grandblade.

LIBERATOR-PRIME

The leader of this unit is the Liberator-Prime. A Liberator-Prime makes 3 attacks rather than 2.

ABILITIES

Paired Weapons: An extra weapon allows a Liberator to feint and parry, creating openings in their opponent's guard. You can re-roll hit rolls of 1 for models armed with more than one Warhammer or Warblade.

Lay Low the Tyrants: If any model from this unit selects an enemy unit with a Wounds characteristic of 5 or more as the target for all of its attacks in a combat phase, add 1 to all of that model's hit rolls in that combat phase.

Sigmarite Shields: You can re-roll save rolls of 1 for this unit if any models from the unit are carrying Sigmarite Shields.

KEYWORDS	ORDER, CELESTIAL, HUMAN, STORMCAST ETERNAL, REDEEMER, LIBERATORS

RETRIBUTORS

Retributors are the wrath of the heavens made flesh. They bring swift and deadly justice to the lands of the Mortal Realms. Their lightning hammers are forged from ensorcelled sigmarite, and by channelling the energy of the storm they can release thunderous bursts of sky-magic that blast the foe to ash.

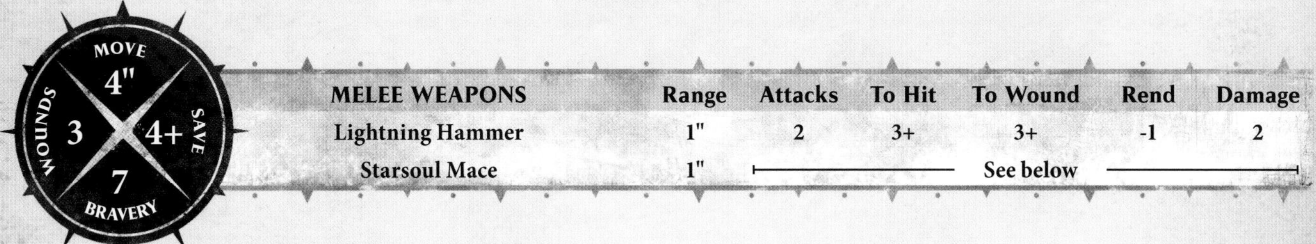

MELEE WEAPONS	Range	Attacks	To Hit	To Wound	Rend	Damage
Lightning Hammer	1"	2	3+	3+	-1	2
Starsoul Mace	1"	See below				

DESCRIPTION

A unit of Retributors has 3 or more models. They are armed with Lightning Hammers. 2 in every 5 models may instead be armed with a Starsoul Mace.

RETRIBUTOR-PRIME

The leader of this unit is the Retributor-Prime. A Retributor-Prime makes 3 attacks rather than 2 with a Lightning Hammer.

ABILITIES

Blast to Ashes: If the hit roll for a model attacking with a Lightning Hammer is 6 or more, that blow strikes with a thunderous blast that inflicts 2 mortal wounds instead of its normal damage. Do not make a wound or save roll for the attack.

Starsoul Mace: A model armed with a Starsoul Mace can make a starblast attack in each combat phase. Pick an enemy unit that is within 1" of the model with the Starsoul Mace. That unit suffers D3 mortal wounds.

KEYWORDS	ORDER, CELESTIAL, HUMAN, STORMCAST ETERNAL, PALADIN, RETRIBUTORS

PROTECTORS

Inexorable and relentless, the Protectors advance. Their stormstrike glaives weave in intricate patterns around them, creating a shield of celestial energy which casts incoming missiles aside. When they reach the enemy's lines, their masterful bladework is turned to a deadlier purpose, dismembering lesser foes and executing leviathans alike.

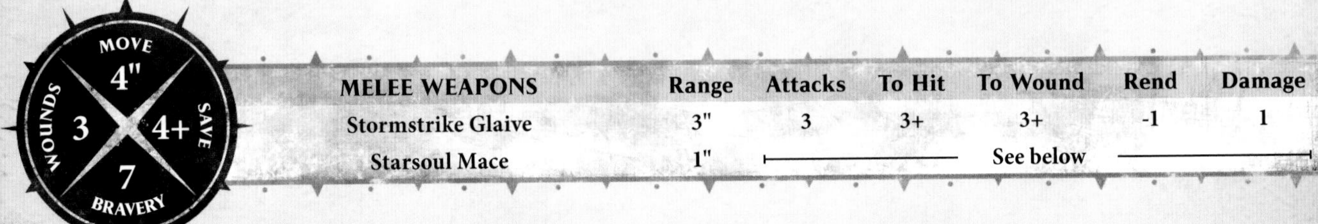

MELEE WEAPONS	Range	Attacks	To Hit	To Wound	Rend	Damage
Stormstrike Glaive	3"	3	3+	3+	-1	1
Starsoul Mace	1"			See below		

DESCRIPTION

A unit of Protectors has 5 or more models. They are armed with Stormstrike Glaives. 2 in every 5 models may instead be armed with a Starsoul Mace.

PROTECTOR-PRIME

The leader of this unit is the Protector-Prime. A Protector-Prime attacking with a Stormstrike Glaive makes 4 attacks rather than 3.

ABILITIES

Deathstrike: A Stormstrike Glaive can slay monstrous foes with a single blow. If the wound roll for a Stormstrike Glaive is 6 or more and the target is a **Monster**, it does D6 Damage instead of 1.

Storm-shield: Arrows are deflected by the Protectors' weaving Glaives. Subtract 1 from the hit rolls of enemy shooting attacks that target a unit of Protectors, or which must cross a unit of Protectors to hit a model that lies beyond them.

Starsoul Mace: A model armed with a Starsoul Mace can make a starblast attack in each combat phase. Pick an enemy unit that is within 1" of the model with the Starsoul Mace. That unit suffers D3 mortal wounds.

KEYWORDS ORDER, CELESTIAL, HUMAN, STORMCAST ETERNAL, PALADIN, PROTECTORS

DECIMATORS

Let the foe come in their teeming hordes, for there to meet them will be the Decimators. With their whirling thunderaxes, these Paladins wade into enemy formations, reaping a bloody toll with every swing. Corpses form grisly piles around the Paladins' feet as these grim destroyers lay low rank after rank, and few foes hold for long in the face of such devastation.

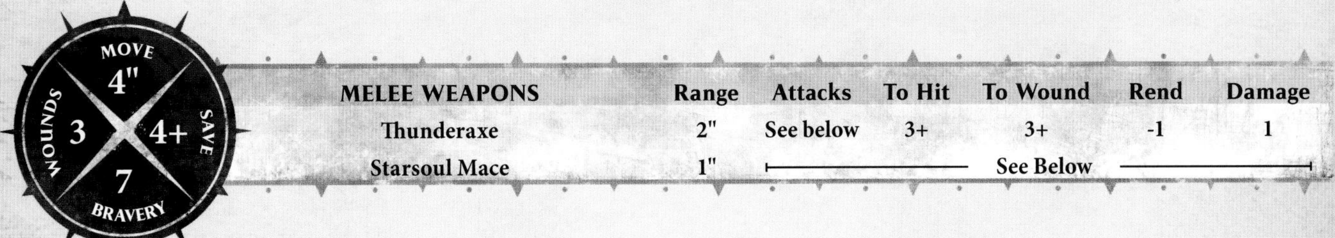

MELEE WEAPONS	Range	Attacks	To Hit	To Wound	Rend	Damage
Thunderaxe	2"	See below	3+	3+	-1	1
Starsoul Mace	1"	See Below				

DESCRIPTION

A unit of Decimators has 5 or more models. They are armed with Thunderaxes. 2 in every 5 models may instead be armed with a Starsoul Mace.

DECIMATOR-PRIME

The leader of this unit is the Decimator-Prime. Add 1 to the wound rolls for a Decimator-Prime.

ABILITIES

Cleaving Blow: A single swing of a Thunderaxe can carve through several foes. When a model attacks with a Thunderaxe, select a target unit and make one attack against it for each model it has within range.

Grim Harvesters: Fear surrounds Decimators as they set about their gory work. Add 2 to the result of battleshock tests made for enemy units that are within 6" of any **DECIMATORS.**

Starsoul Mace: A model armed with a Starsoul Mace can make a starblast attack in each combat phase. Pick an enemy unit that is within 1" of the model with the Starsoul Mace. That unit suffers D3 mortal wounds.

KEYWORDS	ORDER, CELESTIAL, HUMAN, STORMCAST ETERNAL, PALADIN, DECIMATORS

PROSECUTORS

WITH CELESTIAL HAMMERS

The warrior-heralds of Sigmar, Prosecutors soar upon the wings of the storm. Many Prosecutor retinues hurl hammers of magical force as they descend upon their prey, each meteoric impact smiting the enemies of the God-King.

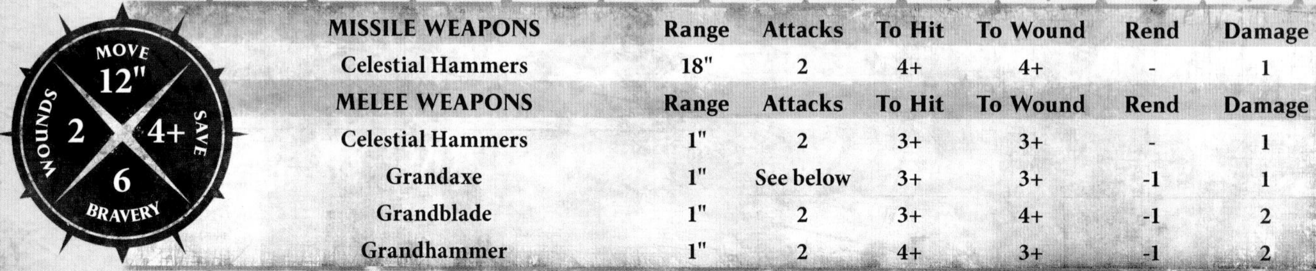

MISSILE WEAPONS	Range	Attacks	To Hit	To Wound	Rend	Damage
Celestial Hammers	18"	2	4+	4+	-	1
MELEE WEAPONS	**Range**	**Attacks**	**To Hit**	**To Wound**	**Rend**	**Damage**
Celestial Hammers	1"	2	3+	3+	-	1
Grandaxe	1"	See below	3+	3+	-1	1
Grandblade	1"	2	3+	4+	-1	2
Grandhammer	1"	2	4+	3+	-1	2

DESCRIPTION

A unit of Prosecutors has 3 or more models. Some units are armed with a Celestial Hammer in each hand, while others go to battle armed with a single Celestial Hammer and carrying a Sigmarite Shield. 1 in every 3 models may instead be armed with a Grandaxe, Grandblade or Grandhammer.

FLY

Prosecutors can fly.

PROSECUTOR-PRIME

The leader of this unit is the Prosecutor-Prime. Trained for brutal melee, he makes 3 attacks rather than 2 in the combat phase.

ABILITIES

Heralds of Righteousness: Roll 3 dice instead of 2 dice when determining the charge move for this unit. In addition, you can declare a charge with this unit if it is within 18" of the enemy rather than 12".

Cleaving Blow: When a model attacks with a Grandaxe, select a target unit and make one attack against it for each model it has within range.

Paired Celestial Hammers: You can re-roll hit rolls of 1 for models armed with more than one Celestial Hammer.

Sigmarite Shields: You can re-roll save rolls of 1 for this unit if any models from the unit are carrying Sigmarite Shields.

KEYWORDS	ORDER, CELESTIAL, HUMAN, STORMCAST ETERNAL, ANGELOS, PROSECUTORS

PROSECUTORS

WITH STORMCALL JAVELINS

Hurtling across the battlefield in a blur of sigmarite, Prosecutors are ideally placed to deliver death to their chosen foes with impunity. To this end, many wield stormcall javelins, which strike their victims with the might of Sigmar's Tempest.

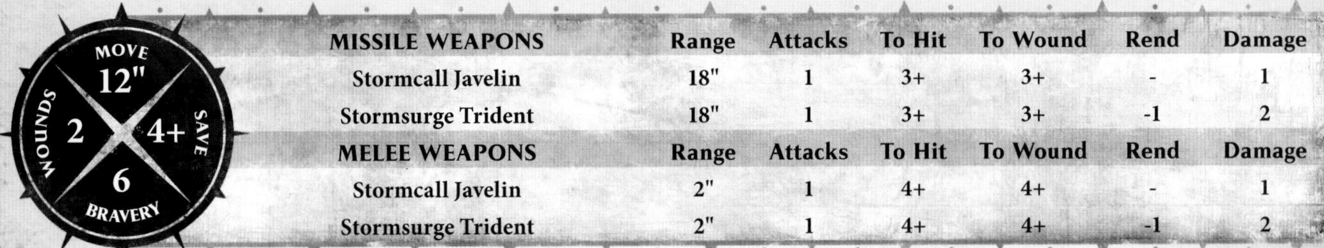

MISSILE WEAPONS	Range	Attacks	To Hit	To Wound	Rend	Damage
Stormcall Javelin	18"	1	3+	3+	-	1
Stormsurge Trident	18"	1	3+	3+	-1	2
MELEE WEAPONS	**Range**	**Attacks**	**To Hit**	**To Wound**	**Rend**	**Damage**
Stormcall Javelin	2"	1	4+	4+	-	1
Stormsurge Trident	2"	1	4+	4+	-1	2

DESCRIPTION

A unit of Prosecutors has 3 or more models. They are armed with Stormcall Javelins and carry Sigmarite Shields. 1 in every 3 models may wield a Stormsurge Trident in place of their Stormcall Javelins.

FLY

Prosecutors can fly.

PROSECUTOR-PRIME

The leader of this unit is the Prosecutor-Prime. Raining death from afar, he makes 2 attacks rather than 1 in the shooting phase.

ABILITIES

Stormcall Javelin: If a Prosecutor throws a Stormcall Javelin at a unit over 9" away, the javelin calls down a bolt of lightning; that attack has Damage 2 instead of 1.

Heralds of Righteousness: Roll 3 dice instead of 2 dice when determining the charge move for this unit. In addition, you can declare a charge with this unit if it is within 18" of the enemy rather than 12".

Sigmarite Shields: You can re-roll save rolls of 1 for this unit if any models from the unit are carrying Sigmarite Shields.

KEYWORDS	ORDER, CELESTIAL, HUMAN, STORMCAST ETERNAL, ANGELOS, PROSECUTORS

CELESTANT-PRIME

HAMMER OF SIGMAR

The first of the Stormcast Eternals, the Celestant-Prime is nothing less than the embodiment of Sigmar's Storm, a living tempest. Bearing the warhammer Ghal Maraz, the Avenging Angel of Azyr crashes into the foe like a thunderbolt, the impact of his blows sweeping away whole enemy ranks at a time. The very comets above are his to command.

MOVE	WOUNDS	SAVE	BRAVERY
12"	8	3+	10

MISSILE WEAPONS	Range	Attacks	To Hit	To Wound	Rend	Damage
The Cometstrike Sceptre	24"	See below				
MELEE WEAPONS	**Range**	**Attacks**	**To Hit**	**To Wound**	**Rend**	**Damage**
Ghal Maraz, the Hammer of Sigmar	2"	2	3+	2+	-3	3

DESCRIPTION

The Celestant-Prime is a single model. He wields Ghal Maraz, the Hammer of Sigmar, and carries the Cometstrike Sceptre. You can only include one Celestant-Prime in your army.

FLY

The Celestant-Prime can fly.

ABILITIES

Cometstrike Sceptre: In your shooting phase, the Celestant-Prime can hold the Cometstrike Sceptre aloft to seize a comet from the heavens, then send it crashing down amid the enemy. If he does, pick a point on the battlefield within range and roll a dice. Each unit within that many inches of that point suffers D3 mortal wounds.

Retribution from On High: Instead of setting up the Celestant-Prime on the battlefield, you must place him to one side and say that he is set up in the Celestial Realm. In each of your movement phases you must declare whether he will strike from the Heavens or remain in the Celestial Realm imbuing Ghal Maraz with additional energies. For each battle round that he remains in the Celestial Realm, add 2 to the Attacks characteristic of Ghal Maraz until the end of the battle.

When the Celestant-Prime strikes from the Heavens, set him up on the battlefield more than 9" from any enemy models. This is his move for that movement phase. Until your next hero phase, subtract 2 from the Bravery of all models in any enemy unit within 12" of him.

Orrery of Celestial Fates: A storm of celestial energy swirls around the Celestant-Prime's feet, granting him mystic insights that aid him in battle. Once per turn, you can change the roll of one dice for the Celestant-Prime to a roll of your choice, before applying any modifiers.

KEYWORDS ORDER, HUMAN, STORMCAST ETERNAL, HERO, CELESTANT-PRIME

WARSCROLL BATTALIONS

The warriors of the Mortal Realms often fight in battalions. Each of these deadly fighting formations consists of several units that are organised and trained to fight alongside each other. The units in warscroll battalions can employ special tactics on the battlefield, making them truly deadly foes.

If you wish, you can organise the units in your army into a warscroll battalion. Doing so will give you access to additional abilities that can be used by the units in the battalion. The information needed to use these powerful formations can be found on the warscroll battalion sheets that we publish for *Warhammer: Age of Sigmar*. Each warscroll battalion sheet lists the units that make it up, and the rules for any additional abilities that units from the warscroll battalion can use.

When you are setting up, you can set up all of the units in a warscroll battalion instead of setting up a single unit. Alternatively, you can set up some of the units from a warscroll battalion, and set up any remaining units individually later on, or you can set up all of the units individually. For example, in a battle where each player takes it in turns to set up one unit, you could set up one, some or all of the units belonging to a warscroll battalion in your army.

On the following pages you will find a selection of warscroll battalions. Usually, a unit can only belong to one battalion, and so can only benefit from a single set of battalion abilities. However, some very large battalions include other, smaller battalions, and in this case it is possible for a unit to benefit from the abilities of two different battalions at the same time.

WARSCROLL BATTALION

STORMCAST ETERNALS

LORDS OF THE STORM

Th[illegible]sed energies of the most powerful heroes of a Strike Chamber do more than just boost St[illegible]st morale; they send a surge of celestial force before them, slaying and driving back their foes.

ORGANISATION

A Lords of the Storm battalion consists of the following units:

- 1 Lord-Celestant or Lord-Celestant on Dracoth
- 1 Lord-Relictor
- 0-1 unit of Gryph-hounds
- 2-5 units chosen in any combination from the following list: Lord-Castellant, Knight-Heraldor, Knight-Vexillor, Knight-Azyros, Knight-Venator

ABILITIES

Aura of Comma[illegible]: [illegible]d 1 to the Bravery of all STORMCAST ETERNAL units from your army that are within 6" of one or more HEROES from this battalion.

Wave of Celestial Might: If at least 3 HEROES from this battalion are within 3" of each other in your opponent's hero phase, roll a dice for each enemy unit that is within 3" of any of them; on a 4+, the enemy unit is battered by a wave of celestial energy and suffers one mortal wound for each STORMCAST ETERNAL HERO within 3" of it. An enemy unit that suffers wounds from the celestial wave must retreat in its subsequent movement phase if possible.

136

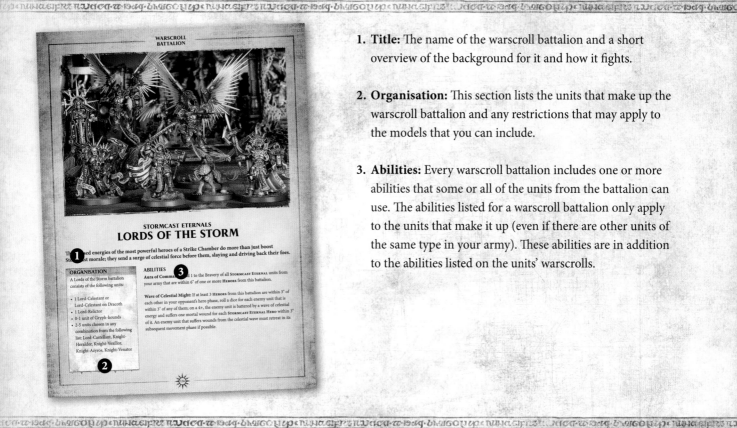

1. **Title:** The name of the warscroll battalion and a short overview of the background for it and how it fights.

2. **Organisation:** This section lists the units that make up the warscroll battalion and any restrictions that may apply to the models that you can include.

3. **Abilities:** Every warscroll battalion includes one or more abilities that some or all of the units from the battalion can use. The abilities listed for a warscroll battalion only apply to the units that make it up (even if there are other units of the same type in your army). These abilities are in addition to the abilities listed on the units' warscrolls.

STORMCAST ETERNALS

LORDS OF THE STORM

The massed energies of the most powerful heroes of a Strike Chamber do more than just boost Stormcast morale; they send a surge of celestial force before them, slaying and driving back their foes.

ORGANISATION

A Lords of the Storm battalion consists of the following units:

- 1 Lord-Celestant or Lord-Celestant on Dracoth
- 1 Lord-Relictor
- 0-1 unit of Gryph-hounds
- 2-5 units chosen in any combination from the following list: Lord-Castellant, Knight-Heraldor, Knight-Vexillor, Knight-Azyros, Knight-Venator

ABILITIES

Aura of Command: Add 1 to the Bravery of all STORMCAST ETERNAL units from your army that are within 6" of one or more HEROES from this battalion.

Wave of Celestial Might: If at least 3 HEROES from this battalion are within 3" of each other in your opponent's hero phase, roll a dice for each enemy unit that is within 3" of any of them; on a 4+, the enemy unit is battered by a wave of celestial energy and suffers one mortal wound for each STORMCAST ETERNAL HERO within 3" of it. An enemy unit that suffers wounds from the celestial wave must retreat in its subsequent movement phase if possible.

STORMCAST ETERNALS

THUNDERHEAD BROTHERHOOD

The Liberators and Judicators of a Thunderhead Brotherhood mesh together in perfect fighting order. Behind a shield wall, the Judicators loose death, while the stalwart Liberators hold the line.

ORGANISATION

A Thunderhead Brotherhood consists of the following units:

- 3 units of Liberators
- 2 units of Judicators

ABILITIES

Sigmarite Shield Wall: If an enemy unit attacks a Judicators unit from a Thunderhead Brotherhood, check whether it is possible to draw a straight line from the attacking unit to a model in the target unit without crossing within 1" of any of the brotherhood's Liberators. If it is not possible, add 1 to any save rolls you make for the Judicators unit.

Wellspring of Thunder: Whilst a unit from this battalion is within 8" of at least two others, it is thundercharged; you can re-roll wound rolls of 1 for models in that unit.

STORMCAST ETERNALS

HAMMERSTRIKE FORCE

With great speed the Prosecutors soar into the heart of the foe, before summoning lightning that brings down celestially charged Retributors. Together, they hit with thunderbolt force.

ORGANISATION

A Hammerstrike Force consists of the following units:

- 2 units of Retributors
- 1 unit of Prosecutors

ABILITIES

Hammerstrike: Instead of setting up the Retributors on the battlefield, you can place either or both units to one side and say that they are set up in the Celestial Realm. In any of your movement phases, you can transport either or both units to the battlefield. When you do so, set them up on the battlefield within 6" of the Hammerstrike Force's Prosecutors. If the Prosecutors have been slain, set up the Retributors more than 9" from any enemy models. In either case, this is their move for that movement phase.

Celestial Supercharge: When a unit of Retributors from the Hammerstrike Force is set up within 6" of its Prosecutors, they are supercharged with celestial energy until the end of your turn. Add 1 to the result of any wound rolls you make for this unit.

STORMCAST ETERNALS

VANGUARD WING

The Prosecutors of a Vanguard Wing empower their Liberator brethren to strike with uncanny might, or to cross the battlefield in a streak of power to launch a timely attack against a vulnerable foe.

ORGANISATION

A Vanguard Wing consists of the following units:

- 3 units of Prosecutors
- 1 unit of Liberators

ABILITIES

Bearers of the Storm: Liberators in a Vanguard Wing are empowered while they are within 8" of the battalion's Prosecutors. If a hit roll for an attack made by these Liberators is 6 or higher, make two wound rolls rather than one.

Stormstreak: Instead of moving in their movement phase, a Vanguard Wing's Liberators can vanish with a crash of thunder, travelling at the speed of a thunderbolt to aid their Prosecutor brethren. Remove the unit from the battlefield, then set it up anywhere within 5" of a unit of Prosecutors from the Vanguard Wing.

STORMCAST ETERNALS

DEVASTATION BROTHERHOOD

Guided to their foe by the Prosecutors, the Paladins of the Devastation Brotherhood plough into enemy battle lines, a crash of sigmarite, fury and celestial energy that hits like a thunderbolt.

ORGANISATION

A Devastation Brotherhood consists of the following units:

- 1 unit of Retributors
- 1 unit of Protectors
- 1 unit of Decimators
- 1 unit of Prosecutors

ABILITIES

Crushing Assault: If models from all of the three PALADIN units inflict wounds on the same enemy unit in the same combat phase, that enemy unit suffers a further D6 mortal wounds at the end of the phase as warriors are smashed to the dirt and trampled beneath their sigmarite-clad footfalls.

Heralds of Ruin: In your hero phase, you can pick an enemy unit within 9" of the brotherhood's Prosecutors. Until your next hero phase, while the Prosecutors are within 9", that unit subtracts one from its Bravery. In addition, before it moves in its movement phase, roll a dice and subtract that many inches from the distance it can move.

STORMCAST ETERNALS
WARDENS OF THE REALMGATE

The Wardens of the Realmgate are a living bulwark, the retinues acting as one to protect their claim. If he deems the situation calls for it, the Lord-Castellant can summon forth further aid from Sigmaron.

ORGANISATION

A Wardens of the Realmgate battalion consists of the following units:

- 1 Lord-Castellant
- 0-1 unit of Gryph-hounds
- 1 unit of Protectors
- 2 units of Liberators
- 1 Baleful Realmgate

ABILITIES

Guardians of the Gate: Do not set up the Baleful Realmgate when setting up the scenery for the battle. Instead, set it up immediately after setting up the battalion's Lord-Castellant.

Summon Reinforcements: Roll a dice in your hero phase if the battalion's Lord-Castellant is within 6" of the Baleful Realmgate. If the result is 4 or higher, you can place a STORMCAST ETERNAL unit (either a new unit from your collection or one that was slain earlier in the battle) within 6" of the Baleful Realmgate and more than 3" from the enemy, adding it to your army as reinforcements. This counts as that unit's move for the following movement phase.

Celestial Barrier: You can re-roll failed save rolls for units from this battalion that are within 6" of the battalion's Protectors.

STORMCAST ETERNALS

WARRIOR CHAMBER

Still crackling with energies from their lightning deployment, the retinues of the Warrior Chamber feed off the rampant celestial forces, using them to mete out violent justice upon their enemies.

ORGANISATION

A Warrior Chamber consists of the following warscroll battalions:

- 1 Lords of the Storm
- 3 Thunderhead Brotherhoods
- 3 Hammerstrike Forces

ABILITIES

Lightning Strike: Instead of setting up a unit from a Warrior Chamber on the battlefield, you can place it to one side and say that it is set up in the Celestial Realm. In any of your movement phases, you can transport the unit to the battlefield. When you do so, set up the unit on the battlefield more than 9" from any enemy models. This is their move for that movement phase.

Wrath of the Storm: If there are at least 50 models from this battalion on the battlefield they are all storm-swathed as their celestial auras coalesce into a palpable force. You can re-roll failed wound rolls for attacks made by these models.

Liberator with grandhammer

Lord-Celestant

Judicator with skybolt bow

STORMCAST ETERNALS
HARBINGER CHAMBER

The Harbinger Chamber uses the might of Sigmar's Tempest to strike deep into the heart of their enemies. Super-charged with celestial energies, the Stormcast Eternals glow with a nimbus of power.

ORGANISATION

A Harbinger Chamber consists of the following warscroll battalions:

- 1 Lords of the Storm
- 3 Vanguard Wings

ABILITIES

Lightning Strike: Instead of setting up a unit from a Harbinger Chamber on the battlefield, you can place it to one side and say that it is set up in the Celestial Realm. In any of your movement phases, you can transport the unit to the battlefield. When you do so, set up the unit on the battlefield more than 9" from any enemy models. This is their move for that movement phase.

Celestial Nimbus: The warriors that form a Harbinger Chamber are charged with a nimbus of celestial energy that lets them anticipate their opponents' actions with preternatural speed. Add 1 to the result of any hit rolls for models from a Harbinger Chamber.

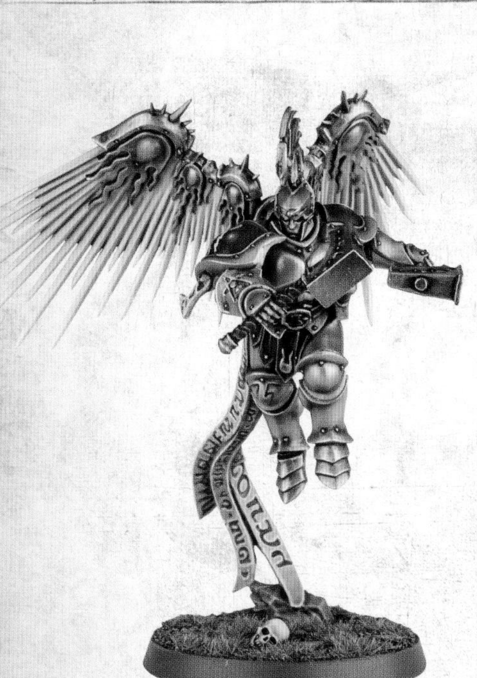

Prosecutor with celestial hammers

Prosecutor-Prime with celestial hammers

STORMCAST ETERNALS

EXEMPLAR CHAMBER

The Exemplar Chamber strikes with sudden fury, smiting their foes and wreaking a terrible vengeance. None may stay their wrath, any losses only spurring them to yet greater violence.

ORGANISATION

An Exemplar Chamber consists of the following warscroll battalions:

- 1 Lords of the Storm
- 3 Devastation Hosts

ABILITIES

Lightning Strike: Instead of setting up a unit from an Exemplar Chamber on the battlefield, you can place it to one side and say that it is set up in the Celestial Realm. In any of your movement phases, you can transport the unit to the battlefield. When you do so, set up the unit on the battlefield more than 9" from any enemy models. This is their move for that movement phase.

Martial Bond: If a unit from an Exemplar Chamber is slain in the combat phase, pick another unit from the chamber within 10" of it. That unit harnesses the celestial energy of their slain brethren to enact swift vengeance upon the foe. Add 1 to the Attacks characteristic of all the unit's melee weapons for the remainder of the battle.

Protector with stormstrike glaive

Retributor with lightning hammer

Retributor with starsoul mace

THE RULES

Warhammer: Age of Sigmar **puts you in command of a force of mighty warriors, monsters and war engines. This rules sheet contains everything you need to know in order to do battle amid strange and sorcerous realms, to unleash powerful magic, darken the skies with arrows, and crush your enemies in bloody combat!**

THE ARMIES

Before the conflict begins, rival warlords gather their most powerful warriors.

In order to play, you must first muster your army from the miniatures in your collection. Armies can be as big as you like, and you can use as many models from your collection as you wish. The more units you decide to use, the longer the game will last and the more exciting it will be! Typically, a game with around a hundred miniatures per side will last for about an evening.

WARSCROLLS & UNITS

All models are described by warscrolls, which provide all of the rules for using them in the game. You will need warscrolls for the models you want to use.

Models fight in units. A unit can have one or more models, but cannot include models that use different warscrolls. A unit must be set up and finish any sort of move as a single group of models, with all models within 1" of at least one other model from their unit. If anything causes a unit to become split up during a battle, it must reform the next time that it moves.

TOOLS OF WAR

In order to fight a battle you will require a tape measure and some dice.

Distances in *Warhammer: Age of Sigmar* are measured in inches ("), between the closest points of the models or units you're measuring to and from. You can measure distances whenever you wish. A model's base isn't considered part of the model – it's just there to help the model stand up – so don't include it when measuring distances.

Warhammer: Age of Sigmar uses six-sided dice (sometimes abbreviated to D6). If a rule requires you to roll a D3, roll a dice and halve the total, rounding fractions up. Some rules allow you to re-roll a dice roll, which means you get to roll some or all of the dice again. You can never re-roll a dice more than once, and re-rolls happen before modifiers to the roll (if any) are applied.

THE BATTLEFIELD

Be they pillars of flame, altars of brass or haunted ruins, the realms are filled with strange sights and deadly obstacles.

Battles in *Warhammer: Age of Sigmar* are fought across an infinite variety of exciting landscapes in the Mortal Realms, from desolate volcanic plains and treacherous sky temples, to lush jungles and cyclopean ruins. The dominion of Chaos is all-pervading, and no land is left untouched by the blight of war. These wildly fantastical landscapes are recreated whenever you play a game of *Warhammer: Age of Sigmar.*

The table and scenery you use constitute your battlefield. A battlefield can be any flat surface upon which the models can stand – for example a dining table or the floor – and can be any size or shape provided it's bigger than 3 feet square.

First you should decide in which of the seven Mortal Realms the battle will take place. For example, you might decide that your battle will take place in the Realm of Fire. Sometimes you'll need to know this in order to use certain abilities. If you can't agree on the realm, roll a dice, and whoever rolls highest decides.

The best battles are fought over lavishly designed and constructed landscapes, but whether you have a lot of scenery or only a small number of features doesn't matter! A good guide is at least 1 feature for every 2 foot square, but less is okay and more can make for a really interesting battle.

To help you decide the placement of your scenery, you can choose to roll two dice and add them together for each 2 foot square area of your battlefield and consult the following table:

Roll	Terrain Features
2-3	No terrain features.
4-5	2 terrain features.
6-8	1 terrain feature.
9-10	2 terrain features.
11-12	Choose from 0 to 3 terrain features.

MYSTERIOUS LANDSCAPES

The landscapes of the Mortal Realms can both aid and hinder your warriors. Unless stated otherwise, a model can be moved across scenery but not through it (so you can't move through a solid wall, or pass through a tree, but can choose to have a model climb up or over them). In addition, once you have set up all your scenery, either roll a dice on the following table or pick a rule from it for each terrain feature:

THE SCENERY TABLE

Roll	Scenery
1	**Damned:** If any of your units are within 3" of this terrain feature in your hero phase, you can declare that one is making a sacrifice. If you do so, the unit suffers D3 mortal wounds, but you can add 1 to all hit rolls for the unit until your next hero phase.
2	**Arcane:** Add 1 to the result of any casting or unbinding rolls made for a wizard within 3" of this terrain feature.
3	**Inspiring:** Add 1 to the Bravery of all units within 3" of this terrain feature.
4	**Deadly:** Roll a dice for any model that makes a run or charge move across, or finishing on, this terrain feature. On a roll of 1 the model is slain.
5	**Mystical:** Roll a dice in your hero phase for each of your units within 3" of this terrain feature. On a roll of 1 the unit is befuddled and can't be selected to cast spells, move or attack until your next hero phase. On a roll of 2-6 the unit is ensorcelled, and you can re-roll failed wound rolls for the unit until your next hero phase.
6	**Sinister:** Any of your units that are within 3" of this terrain feature in your hero phase cause fear until your next hero phase. Subtract 1 from the Bravery of any enemy units that are within 3" of one or more units that cause fear.

THE BATTLE BEGINS

Thunder rumbles high above as the armies take to the battlefield.

You are now ready for the battle to begin, but before it does you must set up your armies for the coming conflict.

SET-UP

Before setting up their armies, both players roll a dice, rolling again in the case of a tie. The player that rolls higher must divide the battlefield into two equal-sized halves; their opponent then picks one half to be their territory. Some examples of this are shown below.

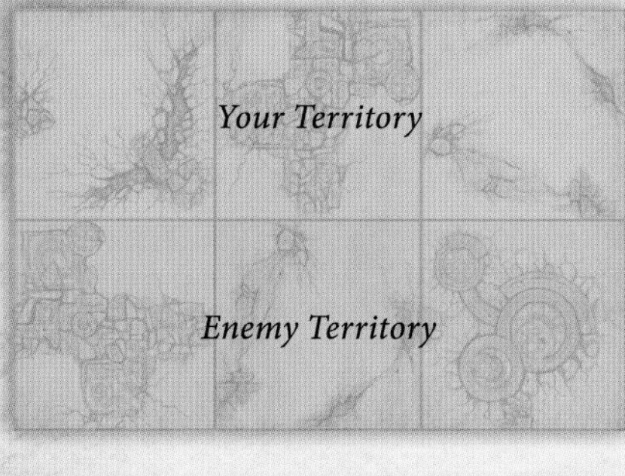

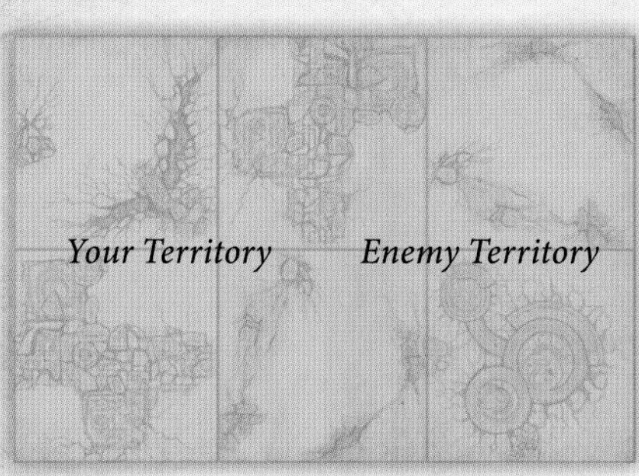

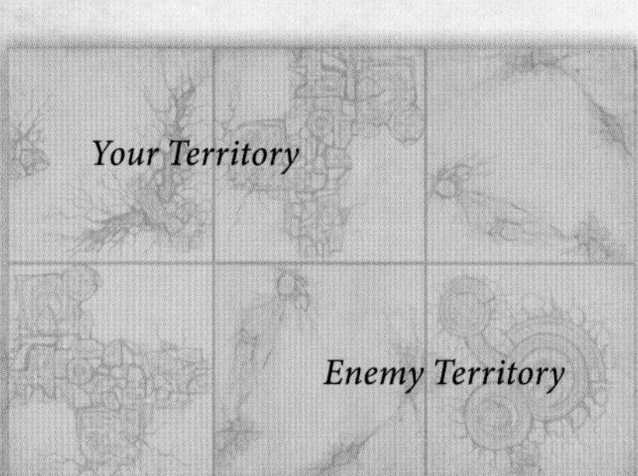

The players then alternate setting up units, one at a time, starting with the player that won the earlier dice roll. Models must be set up in their own territory, more than 12" from enemy territory.

You can continue setting up units until you have set up all the units you want to fight in this battle, or have run out of space. This is your army. Count the number of models in your army – this may come in useful later. Any remaining units are held in reserve, playing no part unless fate lends a hand.

The opposing player can continue to set up units. When they have finished, set-up is complete. The player that finishes setting up first always chooses who takes the first turn in the first battle round.

THE GENERAL

Once you have finished setting up all of your units, nominate one of the models you set up as your general. Your general has a command ability, as described in the rules for the hero phase on the next page.

GLORIOUS VICTORY

In the Mortal Realms battles are brutal and uncompromising – they are fought to the bitter end, with one side able to claim victory because it has destroyed its foe or there are no enemy models left on the field of battle. The victor can immediately claim a **major victory** and the honours and triumphs that are due to them, while the defeated must repair to their lair to lick their wounds and bear the shame of failure.

If it has not been possible to fight a battle to its conclusion or the outcome is not obvious, then a result of sorts can be calculated by comparing the number of models removed from play with the number of models originally set up for the battle for each army. Expressing these as percentages provides a simple way to determine the winner. Such a victory can only be claimed as a **minor victory**. For example, if one player lost 75% of their starting models, and the other player lost 50%, then the player that only lost 50% of their models could claim a minor victory.

Models added to your army during the game (for example, through summoning, reinforcements, reincarnation and so on) do not count towards the number of models in the army, but must be counted among the casualties an army suffers.

SUDDEN DEATH VICTORIES

Sometimes a player may attempt to achieve a sudden death victory. If one army has a third more models than the other, the outnumbered player can choose one objective from the sudden death table after generals are nominated. A **major victory** can be claimed immediately when the objective is achieved by the outnumbered player.

TRIUMPHS

After any sudden death objectives have been chosen, if your army won a major victory in its previous battle, roll a dice and look up the result on the triumph table to the right.

THE SUDDEN DEATH TABLE

Assassinate: The enemy player picks a unit with the **HERO**, **WIZARD**, **PRIEST** or **MONSTER** keyword in their army. Slay the unit that they pick.

Blunt: The enemy player picks a unit with five or more models in their army. Slay the unit that they pick.

Endure: Have at least one model which started the battle on the battlefield still in play at the end of the sixth battle round.

Seize Ground: Pick one terrain feature in enemy territory. Have at least one friendly model within 3" of that feature at the end of the fourth battle round.

THE TRIUMPH TABLE

Roll	Triumph
1-2	**Blessed:** You can change the result of a single dice to the result of your choosing once during the battle.
3-4	**Inspired:** You can re-roll all of the failed hit rolls for one unit in your army in one combat phase.
5-6	**Empowered:** Add 1 to your general's Wounds characteristic.

BATTLE ROUNDS

Mighty armies crash together amid the spray of blood and the crackle of magic.

Warhammer: Age of Sigmar is played in a series of battle rounds, each of which is split into two turns – one for each player. At the start of each battle round, both players roll a dice, rolling again in the case of a tie. The player that rolls highest decides who takes the first turn in that battle round. Each turn consists of the following phases:

1. ***Hero Phase***
   Cast spells and use heroic abilities.
2. ***Movement Phase***
   Move units across the battlefield.
3. ***Shooting Phase***
   Attack with missile weapons.
4. ***Charge Phase***
   Charge units into combat.
5. ***Combat Phase***
   Pile in and attack with melee weapons.
6. ***Battleshock Phase***
   Test the bravery of depleted units.

Once the first player has finished their turn, the second player takes theirs. Once the second player has also finished, the battle round is over and a new one begins.

PRE-BATTLE ABILITIES

Some warscrolls allow you to use an ability 'after set-up is complete'. These abilities are used before the first battle round. If both armies have abilities like this, both players roll a dice, re-rolling in the case of a tie. The player that rolls highest gets to use their abilities first, followed by their opponent.

HERO PHASE

As the armies close in, their leaders use sorcerous abilities, make sacrifices to the gods, or give strident commands.

In your hero phase you can use the wizards in your army to cast spells (see the rules for wizards on the last page of these rules).

In addition, other units in your army may have abilities on their warscrolls that can be used in the hero phase. Generally, these can only be used in your own hero phase. However, if an ability says it can be used in every hero phase, then it can be used in your opponent's hero phase as well as your own. If both players can use abilities in a hero phase, the player whose turn it is gets to use all of theirs first.

COMMAND ABILITY

In your hero phase, your general can use one command ability. All generals have the Inspiring Presence command ability, and some may have more on their warscroll.

Inspiring Presence: Pick a unit from your army that is within 12" of your general. The unit that you pick does not have to take battleshock tests until your next hero phase.

MOVEMENT PHASE

The ground shakes to the tread of marching feet as armies vie for position.

Start your movement phase by picking one of your units and moving each model in that unit until you've moved all the models you want to. You can then pick another unit to move, until you have moved as many of your units as you wish. No model can be moved more than once in each movement phase.

MOVING

A model can be moved in any direction, to a distance in inches equal to or less than the Move characteristic on its warscroll. It can be moved vertically in order to climb or cross scenery, but cannot be moved across other models. No part of the model may move further than the model's Move characteristic.

ENEMY MODELS

When you move a model in the movement phase, you may not move within 3" of any enemy models. Models from your army are friendly models, and models from the opposing army are enemy models.

Units starting the movement phase within 3" of an enemy unit can either remain stationary or retreat. If you choose to retreat, the unit must end its move more than 3" away from all enemy units. If a unit retreats, then it can't shoot or charge later that turn (see below).

RUNNING

When you pick a unit to move in the movement phase, you can declare that it will run. Roll a dice and add the result to the Move characteristic of all models in the unit for the movement phase. A unit that runs can't shoot or charge later that turn.

FLYING

If the warscroll for a model says that the model can fly, it can pass across models and scenery as if they were not there. It still may not finish the move within 3" of an enemy in the movement phase, and if it is already within 3" of an enemy it can only retreat or remain stationary.

SHOOTING PHASE

A storm of death breaks over the battle as arrows fall like rain and war machines hurl their deadly payloads.

In your shooting phase you can shoot with models armed with missile weapons.

Pick one of your units. You may not pick a unit that ran or retreated this turn. Each model in the unit attacks with all of the missile weapons it is armed with (see Attacking). After all of the models in the unit have shot, you can choose another unit to shoot with, until all units that can shoot have done so.

CHARGE PHASE

Howling bloodcurdling war cries, warriors hurl themselves into battle to slay with blade, hammer and claw.

Any of your units within 12" of the enemy in your charge phase can make a charge move. Pick an eligible unit and roll two dice. Each model in the unit can move this number in inches. You may not pick a unit that ran or retreated this turn, nor one that is within 3" of the enemy.

The first model you move must finish within ½" of an enemy model. If that's impossible, the charge has failed and no models in the charging unit can move in this phase. Once you've moved all the models in the unit, you can pick another eligible unit to make a charge, until all units that can charge have done so.

COMBAT PHASE

Carnage engulfs the battlefield as the warring armies tear each other apart.

Any unit that has charged or has models within 3" of an enemy unit can attack with its melee weapons in the combat phase.

The player whose turn it is picks a unit to attack with, then the opposing player must attack with a unit, and so on until all eligible units on both sides have attacked once each. If one side completes all its attacks first, then the other side completes all of its remaining attacks, one unit after another. No unit can be selected to attack more than once in each combat phase. An attack is split into two steps: first the unit piles in, and then you make attacks with the models in the unit.

Step 1: When you pile in, you may move each model in the unit up to 3" towards the closest enemy model. This will allow the models in the unit to get closer to the enemy in order to attack them.

Step 2: Each model in the unit attacks with all of the melee weapons it is armed with (see Attacking).

BATTLESHOCK PHASE

Even the bravest heart may quail when the horrors of battle take their toll.

In the battleshock phase, both players must take battleshock tests for units from their army that have had models slain during the turn. The player whose turn it is tests first.

To make a battleshock test, roll a dice and add the number of models from the unit that have been slain this turn. For each point by which the total exceeds the highest Bravery characteristic in the unit, one model in that unit must flee and is removed from play. Add 1 to the Bravery characteristic being used for every 10 models that are in the unit when the test is taken.

You must choose which models flee from the units you command.

ATTACKING

Blows hammer down upon the foe, inflicting bloody wounds.

When a unit attacks, you must first pick the target units for the attacks that the models in the unit will make, then make all of the attacks, and finally inflict any resulting damage on the target units.

The number of attacks a model can make is determined by the weapons that it is armed with. The weapon options a model has are listed in its description on its warscroll. Missile weapons can be used in the shooting phase, and melee weapons can be used in the combat phase. The number of attacks a model can make is equal to the Attacks characteristic for the weapons it can use.

PICKING TARGETS

First, you must pick the target units for the attacks. In order to attack an enemy unit, an enemy model from that unit must be in range of the attacking weapon (i.e. within the maximum distance, in inches, of the Range listed for the weapon making the attack), and visible to the attacker (if unsure, stoop down and get a look from behind the attacking model to see if the target is visible). For the purposes of determining visibility, an attacking model can see through other models in its unit.

If a model has more than one attack, you can split them between potential target units as you wish. If a model splits its attacks between two or more enemy units, resolve all of the attacks against one unit before moving onto the next one.

MAKING ATTACKS

Attacks can be made one at a time, or, in some cases, you can roll the dice for attacks together. The following attack sequence is used to make attacks one at a time:

1. Hit Roll: Roll a dice. If the roll equals or beats the attacking weapon's To Hit characteristic, then it scores a hit and you must make a wound roll. If not, the attack fails and the attack sequence ends.

2. Wound Roll: Roll a dice. If the roll equals or beats the attacking weapon's To Wound characteristic, then it causes damage and the opposing player must make a save roll. If not, the attack fails and the attack sequence ends.

3. Save Roll: The opposing player rolls a dice, modifying the roll by the attacking weapon's Rend characteristic. For example, if a weapon has a -1 Rend characteristic, then 1 is subtracted from the save roll. If the result equals or beats the Save characteristic of the models in the target unit, the wound is saved and the attack sequence ends. If not, the attack is successful, and you must determine damage on the target unit.

4. Determine Damage: Once all of the attacks made by a unit have been carried out, each successful attack inflicts a number of wounds equal to the Damage characteristic of the weapon. Most weapons have a Damage characteristic of 1, but some can inflict 2 or more wounds, allowing them to cause grievous injuries to even the mightiest foe, or to cleave through more than one opponent with but a single blow!

In order to make several attacks at once, all of the attacks must have the same To Hit, To Wound, Rend and Damage characteristics, and must be directed at the same enemy unit. If this is the case, make all of the hit rolls at the same time, then all of the wound rolls, and finally all of the save rolls; then add up the total number of wounds caused.

INFLICTING DAMAGE

After all of the attacks made by a unit have been carried out, the player commanding the target unit allocates any wounds that are inflicted to models from the unit as they see fit (the models do not have to be within range or visible to an attacking unit). When inflicting damage, if you allocate a wound to a model, you must keep on allocating wounds to that model until either it is slain, or no more wounds remain to be allocated.

Once the number of wounds suffered by a model during the battle equals its Wounds characteristic, the model is slain. Place the slain model to one side – it is removed from play. Some warscrolls include abilities that allow wounds to be healed. A healed wound no longer has any effect. You can't heal wounds on a model that has been slain.

MORTAL WOUNDS

Some attacks inflict mortal wounds. Do not make hit, wound or save rolls for a mortal wound – just allocate the wounds to models from the target unit as described above.

COVER

If all models in a unit are within or on a terrain feature, you can add 1 to all save rolls for that unit to represent the cover they receive from the terrain. This modifier does not apply in the combat phase if the unit you are making saves for made a charge move in the same turn.

WIZARDS

The realms are saturated with magic, a seething source of power for those with the wit to wield it.

Some models are noted as being a wizard on their warscroll. You can use a wizard to cast spells in your hero phase, and can also use them to unbind spells in your opponent's hero phase. The number of spells a wizard can attempt to cast or unbind each turn is detailed on its warscroll.

CASTING SPELLS

All wizards can use the spells described below, as well as any spells listed on their warscroll. A wizard can only attempt to cast each spell once per turn.

To cast a spell, roll two dice. If the total is equal to or greater than the casting value of the spell, the spell is successfully cast.

If a spell is cast, the opposing player can choose any one of their wizards that is within 18" of the caster, and that can see them, and attempt to unbind the spell before its effects are applied. To unbind a spell, roll two dice. If the roll beats the roll used to cast the spell, then the spell's effects are negated. Only one attempt can be made to unbind a spell.

ARCANE BOLT

Arcane Bolt has a casting value of 5. If successfully cast, pick an enemy unit within 18" of the caster and which is visible to them. The unit you pick suffers D3 mortal wounds.

MYSTIC SHIELD

Mystic Shield has a casting value of 6. If successfully cast, pick the caster, or a friendly unit within 18" of the caster and which is visible to them. You can add 1 to all save rolls for the unit you pick until the start of your next hero phase.

THE MOST IMPORTANT RULE

In a game as detailed and wide-ranging as *Warhammer: Age of Sigmar*, there may be times when you are not sure exactly how to resolve a situation that has come up during play. When this happens, have a quick chat with your opponent, and apply the solution that makes the most sense to you both (or seems the most fun!). If no single solution presents itself, both of you should roll a dice, and whoever rolls higher gets to choose what happens. Then you can get on with the fighting!